honeybees from close up

By ARTHUR M. DINES

Photographs by STEPHEN DALTON

CASSELL · LONDON

CASSELL AND COMPANY LTD
35 Red Lion Square, London WC1
Melbourne, Sydney, Toronto
Johannesburg, Auckland

First published in Great Britain 1968
S.B.N. 304 93164 0
Phototypeset by BAS Printers Ltd
Wallop, Hampshire
Printed in the United States of America
F. 168

honeybees from close up

Miss Whyte Johnstone, without whose skill and willing help many of the photographs in this book could not have been taken.

contents

illustrations

acknowledgments

In this book the author sets out to share with readers the pleasure of a lifetime spent in studying and working with the bee. In doing so he must acknowledge his debt to the many writers and scientists on whose work he has drawn so freely throughout. Three books that have been valuable sources of information are *The Hive and the Honey Bee*, edited by Roy A. Grout; *The World of the Honey Bee*, by Dr. Colin Butler; and *The Behavior and Social Life of Honey Bees*, by Ronald Ribbands. Acknowledgment is also freely given to various publications of the Bee Research Association, and above all to the work and writings of Professor Karl von Frisch.

1. the honeybee

The life of insects in general is remote from our common experience; yet by a very large margin they form the most numerous group of animals in the world. Some 700,000 species have been classified and named. They have been extremely successful in adapting themselves to a wide range of climates, diets, and other conditions. There is hardly a plant or animal substance on which some insect has not learned to feed either on land or under it from the tropics to the Arctic Circle.

The body plan of insects sets a limit to their size, but gives them other advantages. They have a highly protective external skeleton of chitin—a tough, waterproof, heat-insulating material. Their powerful jaws and other external organs also consist of chitin. The thickness, hardness, and flexibility of the outer body shell varies with different species, according to their particular way of life, and even between an insect's different parts according to their function. In chitin, natural chemistry has produced a material comparable in properties to man-made plastics.

The breathing system is ideal for insects within the normal-size range, but efficiency decreases as the size increases. Air is taken in through a series of holes, called spiracles, along the sides of the body. A branched network of tubes carries the oxygen direct to the various organs. Oxygen is not carried in the blood-stream. The waste carbon dioxide travels back along the tracheae by an exchange process. This is a simple and efficient system in the smaller insects, whose tubes are short. But the bigger the body, the longer and more branched are the tracheae, resulting in severe reductions in the rate of gas exchange. The organs of large insects receive oxygen only in very limited amounts. Consequently the larger insect tends to be lethargic and a poor competitor in the struggle for existence.

The honeybee is a fortunate member of the insect world; its size has fostered the evolution of highly efficient skeletal, muscular, and breathing systems. The honeybee's complex social life, which is a source of constant fascination to us, is the result of extra-ordinary developments in its senses. Despite all the exciting discoveries in recent years, these senses still hold some mysteries for us.

Bees and wasps are two groups of insects having certain physical similarities, but there is a basic difference between them: Bees' food consists of pollen and nectar obtained from flowers, whereas wasps are partly or wholly carnivorous. Each group has both social and solitary species. Bumblebees and the social wasps live in family communities that exist for one season only. In the spring each group starts with a single female, the queen, who has been hibernating. She makes a small nest in which she lays a few eggs, and gathers food for the resulting larvae as they hatch. This first brood become workers that assist with the food gathering and build extensions to the nest. The queen is now able to lay a progressively larger number of eggs, until eventually there are enough workers to allow her to stay in the nest all the time. By late summer the colony has reached its maximum size and prosperity. Then a number of young queens and males are produced, and they mate. With the arrival of cold weather, the well-fed young queens go into hibernation, and the rest of the community die off.

The honeybee colony differs markedly from these in that it has a continuous existence, maintaining itself as a social unit right through the winter months. This is an extraordinary achievement. To accomplish it, the honeybee learned to gather food in large quantities and evolved methods to preserve and store it. It learned to conserve heat and to regulate the humidity and air flow in its hive,

Every bee in the colony is the offspring of a single queen. The colony has a complex organization, and its members perform highly specialized tasks.

so that life can go on with the least possible expenditure of energy during the hard months. Because the honeybee has succeeded in doing all these things it can build much larger colonies than can the other bees and thus begin its life earlier in the spring. It has not only increased its chances of survival; it has also established itself over a wider range of climate than is usual for a single species of insect. Contributing to the honeybee's longevity is its swarming system of reproduction, which reduces the hazards that individuals must face.

The complex organization of the honeybee colony, with its groups of members performing highly specialized tasks and with its apparent power to control its own destiny, has long been a source of wonder. It has been common in the past to compare bee life to human civilization. This is false reasoning. The colony is not composed of many small groups of bees that have gathered together for mutual benefit and protection; instead, like the bumblebees and the social wasps, it is a single family. In normal circumstances each of the thousands of bees within the community is the offspring of one mother, the queen. So utterly interdependent are they all that separate existence for any one bee is impossible. It is the colony itself that has individuality, a superorganism in which each bee is a working part or organ. The laying of eggs by the queen maintains the colony's life by renewing the working parts as they wear out; but the egg laying does not by itself constitute an act of reproduction. That comes when the colony divides itself at swarming time, an event that involves the production of a new queen.

The phrase 'a swarm of bees' describes a sight familiar to many people: a great mass of insects on the wing, or resting in a tight cluster on the branch of a tree, in a shrub, or on a fence. If it is a prime swarm from a hive, it is accompanied by the mother queen and is a pioneering unit on its way to establish a new home elsewhere. By migrating in swarms, the honeybee can move into fresh territory without great risk to the species; it is the simple division of the colonies at a time of prosperity, even of overabundance.

Many bees have been left behind in the old hive, and thousands of mature larvae will soon be added to the community. More important, before the swarm left preparations were made to provide a new young queen to replace the one that was to leave. Thus the superorganism reproduces itself while insuring its own continuance.

The queen is the vital member of the colony, the source of its abundant life. She is distinguished in the hive from the mass of workers partly by her greater length—about seven-eighths of an inch to the worker's five-eighths of an inch—and partly by her different shape. Her abdomen is slender and tapered and longer than the worker's, and her wings lie more neatly folded along her back. The queen bee exercises no direct ruling function; in fact she herself is ruled by the life of the hive. Her one job is to lay eggs; and except for the brief mating flights and the possible migration with a swarm, her whole life is spent inside the hive. Sunny days among the flowers are not for her. She normally receives a great deal of

Except for brief mating flights, the queen's only task is to lay eggs. She is distinguished by a long, tapered abdomen, and wings that lie neatly folded along her back.

Although shorter than the queen, the drones are broader and heavier. Their sole function is to mate with the queen.

attention, and her very presence has a vital effect on all the bees; but should she begin to fail in her job, the colony would soon produce a successor and discard her without ceremony.

The male bees are called drones. Their sole function is the mating of young queens. These are the biggest members of the colony, for although shorter than the queen, they are broader and heavier. The number of drones in a hive rarely exceeds a few hundred. They are present only during the summer months, for the colony eliminates them at the end of the season. Nevertheless, this is abundant provision by Nature, for the number of queens reared in each colony is very small, and each has a single brief mating period in a lifetime of perhaps several years.

The existence of a separate worker caste, in addition to normal males and females, is a phenomenon of the social insects. It occurs among ants and termites, as well as among bees and wasps. The workers are really females that have, through a controlled diet in the growing stage, failed to develop their sex organs. By far the most numerous in the colony, the workers perform the main tasks, such as gathering food, building the nest, and tending the young. Worker bees and wasps also act as guards, actively defending the home with their stings.

With its specialized body organs and highly developed senses, the worker honeybee is well adapted for carrying out its manifold duties, both inside and outside the hive. It is the little worker that flits from flower to flower in the warm days, extending its tongue down inside them to suck the sweet nectar, or gathering the golden pollen from the anthers onto its hind legs in order to bring it home. The well-being of the colony is at all times dependent on the workers, who may number as many as 80,000 in midsummer. Because there is such a highly dev-

The real tasks of the colony, such as gathering food, building and defending the nest, and caring for the young, are performed by the numerous worker bees.

eloped system of communication between them, they seem to possess a 'mass mind' that determines the behavior of the whole organism.

The existence of three kinds of bees in the hive raises questions as to what control the colony has in determining their nature. The answers, so far as they are known, provide us with some of the most interesting facts of bee life. One is the predetermination of sex. Whether a particular egg will produce a drone or a female is under deliberate control, apparently by the queen, but possibly by the workers after the egg is laid.

As is common among insects, the eggs laid by the queen do not hatch into miniature adults but into wormlike larvae. Fed by workers, they grow rapidly; they are raised in the honeycomb cells of the hive. At the end of the feeding phase they are sealed within their cells where they undergo the changes known as metamorphosis, from which they emerge as full-grown adults. The process corresponds to the life of a caterpillar, which spins itself into a cocoon when fully grown and emerges as a perfect butterfly some time later.

The body of the adult bee is that of the typical insect, with three distinct sections—head, thorax, and abdomen—joined by short, flexible constrictions. The head carries the mouthparts, eyes, and antennae on the outside, and the brain and certain glands inside. Externally, the thorax has the organs of locomotion: two pairs of wings on top and three pairs of legs below. Internally it contains the muscles that operate the wings and legs, plus more glands and minimal passages for the food channel, main blood vessel, nerve cord, and air ducts. The largest section is the abdomen, with the digestive and excretory systems, blood-circulating mechanism, wax glands in a worker, and a sting in both worker and

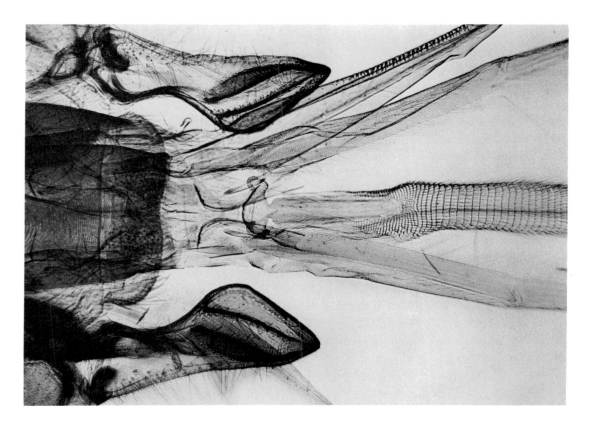

The mouthparts of the worker bee are perfectly suited to the gathering of nectar and the construction of the wax comb.

queen. The ovaries of the queen and the rudimentary ones of the worker are there, as well as the sex organs of both queen and drone. The abdomen pulsates lengthwise to produce the breathing action. Three pairs of spiracles are on the sides of the thorax, and seven pairs are on the abdomen.

Each of the main divisions of the body retains evidence of the larval segments in what appear to be overlapping plates forming the exterior shell. Actually the chitin shell is a continuous layer that varies in thickness and is folded so as to give both strength and flexibility. The visible outer portions are relatively thick and hard, whereas the inner folds are soft to allow freedom of movement. This is particularly true of the abdomen. The muscular system is attached to this exo-skeleton. The whole body is covered with hairs of several types. Most are soft and feathery and touch-sensitive; some are spiky and presumably protective.

Of the manifold adaptions in insect body structure, the mouthparts show the widest variation. Every species is well equipped to deal with its own particular food material, and the proboscis of the honeybee is no exception. The worker especially has a most efficient arrangement for extracting the liquid nectar from flowers and passing it to a sac within the body for transport to the hive. In addition its jaws, or mandibles, are highly adapted for constructing the wax honeycombs.

The three pairs of legs, all five-jointed, terminate in double-clawed feet that have retractable suction pads for walking on smooth surfaces. Each pair, however, differs in other respects. They increase in length from front to rear; the front legs, as is usual in insects, have shaped notches, each containing a row of spines, for cleaning the antennae. The worker, on the tarsi of the front legs, also has rows of hairs that are used as brushes for cleaning loose pollen from the head and mouthparts after visits to flowers. There are no special organs on the second pair, but the hind legs of the worker are highly specialized for the handling and transport of pollen. On the flattened wide tibia is a pattern of strong curved hairs, and as pollen is gathered it is packed there to be carried home. The large knee joint below is a powerful toothed press, and there are collecting brushes that help transfer the pollen from other parts of the body and from one hind leg to the other. All these are used in the packing process. The final result, the 'pollen basket,' so readily visible because of its bulk and color, is a masterpiece of neatness and delicate balance.

Insect wings are not modified limbs, like those of birds, but outgrowths

The three pairs of legs are all five-jointed and increase in length from front to rear. The much-magnified photographs (left) show part of a worker's hind leg, with the pollen comb in the knee joint, and (right) the clawed foot.

from the chitin of the thorax. The branched 'veins,' which are the hardened remains of tracheae present during the growth in the pupal stage, act as strengthening ribs. The wings have no external muscles; all are within the thorax. They do not flap; instead their action is similar to that of oars in rowing a boat, involving in the same way a change of surface angle during the complete stroke. The large front wings are the principal drivers, the rear ones being concerned largely with steering and aerobatics, which they control through an elaborate lever system at the bases. Power is supplied by muscles that produce a rhythmic alteration in the shape of the thorax itself. In straight flight the fore and rear wings can be hooked together to synchronize their movements and give maximum speed.

The worker bee, having a maximum speed of about 15 mph, is capable of performing very rapid maneuvers. Its four wings can operate independently, and it can actually fly backward for a foot or two. The powerful drone is able not only to fly long distances in his search for a mate, but also to support a queen in flight during the mating act.

It is common knowledge that a worker bee has a sting, and that it can be used with considerable effect. The sting is really a modification of the ovipositor, found in female insects and used to place eggs in position as they are laid. This explains why the sting is situated at the tip of the abdomen, as well as why drones do not have them. The sting of a queen is slightly curved and smooth, so that it can be readily withdrawn after use; it is never used except in a fight with a rival.

Insect wings are outgrowths from the external skeleton of the thorax. A network of 'veins' acts as strengthening ribs. The front edge of the rear wing shows hooks for attachment to fore wing.

The sting is a modification of the ovipositor. The barbed lancet in this sting complex is clearly visible outside its sheath.

The worker's sting is straight and consists of a pair of finely pointed and barbed lancets inside a sheath, from which they can be protruded. Once injected into a victim, they work forward in a reciprocating action, aided by the grip the barbs provide. Two lobes, acting as pumps, propel the poison from its sac down through a channel in the sheath, to be worked into the wound. From human flesh, at least, the bee is rarely able to withdraw its sting, for the barbs catch under the skin. The bee pulls itself away, leaving behind the whole organ, including the muscles, which by reflex action continue to pump in the venom.

With its rear abdominal plates and muscles ruptured, the unfortunate bee will soon die; but the colony has lost only a small part of itself in its own defense.

The chemical composition of bee venom is complex. It is a protein poison similar to snake venom, though fortunately produced in smaller quantities. Few people are likely to suffer any serious ill effects after being stung by a bee on an ordinary fleshy part of the body. The sting is always painful at the time, and the subsequent swelling can be quite frightening. Medical attention may be necessary for a person unusually sensitive to the poison, who may lose consciousness or develop a severe rash. There are really no simple remedies, for the venom quickly spreads into the blood stream, but there is a psychological benefit from some of the standard treatments. For the serious cases, adrenalin is the usual medication. Young children, who rarely suffer severe swelling from a bee sting, as do some adults, tend to forget the experience more quickly.

Beekeepers, who get a certain amount of regular stinging, never cease to feel the sharp pain on each occasion, although they learn to ignore it. But over a period of time their blood builds up a resistance to the poison so that aftereffects become negligible. There is a tradition that beekeepers, through being regularly stung, never suffer from rheumatism. This is not wholly true, but recent scientific work does lend some support to the idea, and bee venom is being studied further in relation to this group of diseases.

It is fairly certain that our honeybee, *Apis mellifera*, originated in southern Asia, together with three other related species that are still there. By its powers of adaptability it spread itself eastward to China, westward to the Mediterranean countries, southwest into Africa, and perhaps finally northward in Europe almost to the Arctic Circle.

Wherever the honeybee established itself it was modified by natural selection, until there were a number of 'geographic races,' each particularly suited to survive in its own habitat. For instance, in northern Europe there exist strains of dark-colored bees, often called 'blacks' by beekeepers. They are adapted to the long winters and frequently indifferent summers of their native lands. Characteristically they are very thrifty and are able to survive the winter on a minimum amount of stores; they do not make such large colonies as some others, and they rarely store really large quantities of honey. The Italian race, on the other hand, is a lighter color, much more prolific, and capable of gathering very large crops of honey in suitable circumstances. It is the Italian bee, above all others, that has been exploited in recent times for the commercial production of honey. In good climates it is probably unsurpassed, but it is not always successful if left to itself in areas where winters tend to be severe. Future attempts to breed even better strains of bees are almost certain to include the Italian branch.

There were no honeybees in the New World before European settlers took them there. The Portuguese established some in Brazil around 1530, but the first recorded shipment into North America came from Holland in 1638. Others from Britain and France must have soon followed. The Italian bee does not seem to have been known in America until 1859. European farmers brought with them their fruit trees and clovers and other crop plants that bees work, but many native American plants are abundant yielders of nectar and pollen. Once established, the bees flourished across the continent, often ahead of the human colonists.

Man's first interest in the honeybee was not in its fascinating life story (of which he had no inkling at that time) but in the delicious food it produces. Honey was highly regarded as a human food long before the days of written history. A prehistoric cave painting in Valencia, Spain—an estimate places it at about 7000 B.C.—shows honey being taken from a wild bees' nest. Greek and Roman writers make frequent references to honey and beeswax and beekeeping, and Moses' promise to the Children of Israel was 'a land flowing with milk and honey.' Today, although the sugarcane and sugar beet make us no longer dependent on honey as a main sweetening agent, we appreciate more than ever the delicate flavors and nutritive value of this completely natural food. And because its simple sugars are so readily assimilable, honey is valuable also for dietary purposes.

We are able to delight our palates with different kinds of honey because each is characteristic of the plant from which the original nectar came. Although some get mixed in the hive to form a natural blend, the nature of nectar does produce a considerable number of different honeys. The diversity of flavor and aroma are

Bees, who rarely attack unless provoked, die soon after stinging. The bee at the right is about to insert his sting in a human hand.

due to the large variety of aromatic substances in the nectar of different plants. So we have clover honey, orange honey, and many others, including the heather honey of northern Europe and the thyme honey of Greece, which have always been highly prized.

For bees, honey is the principal food during the flowerless months of winter, and a reserve supply of sugar at any time. Its accumulation is the result of prodigious labor by many thousands of workers in the summer. They gather the nectar, and then, by elaborate chemical and physical processing, convert that liquid into the highly concentrated and stable product that is honey.

Practically all flowers produce some nectar, but it varies greatly in quantity and sugar content. Not all of it is available to the honeybee, for in some cases the bee's tongue is not long enough to reach it. Such flowers may be visited by butterflies and moths or the larger bumblebee. Where they have a choice, bees will always work those plants that secrete good quantities of nectar with the highest proportion of sugar in it. In times of scarcity they will gather whatever they can, including the product from the extra-floral nectaries of some plants and sometimes the sweet juices of damaged fruits. Whatever the origins of nectar secretion, there is no doubt that it now serves the purpose of attracting pollinating insects to the flowers. Occasionally it is produced in such large quantities that it even drips from some of the flowers.

Apis mellifera, the European honeybee, at work.

12

When we think of a pound of honey and compare it with the capacity of the honey sac in a little forager bee—about one five-thousandth of an ounce—we begin to realize the enormous amount of time and labor that go into its production. Even so, the honey sac is large compared with the amount of nectar to be obtained in one visit to a flower. The least number of ordinary small flowers visited by a single bee on a single foraging trip is about fifty. The average is far more, for six hundred to eight hundred visits are common. Nectar-gathering trips average about an hour. Finally, in the process of converting nectar into honey, about half of it in weight evaporates. So the pound of honey represents more than thirty thousand foraging trips and countless visits to flowers. The figures become astronomical when measuring one colony's total honey production for an entire season. In favorable situations, and with human management, three hundred pounds in a single hive is possible. Even in natural circumstances, when the honey totals only one-tenth of this amount, it still means a lot of flying miles.

The dependence of many plants upon bees for pollination is well known. Pollen grains, so small as to look like colored dust to the naked eye, are beautiful in their variety of shapes and sizes when seen under the microscope. Each grain is a male fertilizing agent, and seed cannot develop until a union has taken place between each female ovule and elements of a pollen grain of the same plant species. Usually an individual flower cannot fertilize itself, but depends on some outside agency to transfer pollen from another of its kind. With some plant families—grasses and many trees, for instance—the wind is the agent of cross fertilization, but those higher on the evolutionary scale that have petaled flowers nearly all rely on insects.

At some stage in the evolution of the flowering plants the ancestors of bees must have begun to use them as a source of food. Then through long phases of mutual influence, as the plants came to depend on the bee for their own propagation, so the honeybee became completely dependent on these plants for its food and, directly or indirectly, for its nesting materials. There is complete interdependence. Without bees, most of the flowers we know would not exist, and neither would our familiar fruits, or the clovers and similar plants that are used for cattle fodder. Man's debt to the bee goes beyond the honey it provides.

Because of its economic value in producing honey and beeswax, and because of its fascinating life story, the honeybee has been studied more than any other insect. Not only has this work laid foundations for the study of other insects, both beneficial and harmful, but also because of it, certain biological principles having more general application have been discovered. A further stimulus to the study of the honeybee has come with the recognition of its value in crop pollination. At the present time nearly all the major countries of the world employ scientists for full-time research into more efficient exploitation of the bee and its products, as well as its physiology and behavior.

2. within the hive

The mandibles of the honeybee, perfect for the delicate molding of wax, are too soft and smooth to bite off stubborn materials in the way many other insects do when making a nest. The honeybee must find some suitable cavity from which nothing more than small loose particles of rubbish need be removed. The preferred choice is a dry cavity, with a minimum volume of one cubic foot and direct protection against rain and snow, that is sufficiently enclosed to defend against enemies. Almost invariably the bees will select a place sheltered from strong winds.

Most commonly a wild honeybees' nest is in a hollow of a tree trunk. Its location, some distance above the ground, will prevent interference by many potential enemies, and usually the entrance to the hollow will be small enough to be easily defended. However, it is not unusual in warm climates to find colonies in rock clefts. Occasionally a colony may make its nest entirely in the open, with combs depending from the branch of a tree, in the manner of certain tropical bees. The roofs and hollow walls of human dwellings provide stray swarms of bees with ideal nesting places, and they frequently take advantage of them. The many types of hives used to domesticate bees provide adequately for the insects' basic requirements. The differences are due to the climate and to the convenience and taste of the individual beekeeper; they reflect his knowledge, skill, and tradition.

Hanging from the upper surfaces of the nest cavity, at approximately one-and-one-half-inch intervals across the space, are those marvels of natural engineering, the wax honeycombs. Each has a double-sided network of cells, separated by a midrib, and a total thickness averaging less than one inch. This leaves a working space for the bees between the surfaces. Most people are familiar with the cells' hexagonal shape and the amazing uniformity of their structure, but only close study of a comb will reveal the efficiency of its design. The ideal shape of a cell for a wormlike larva would be round, but cells built side by side in this fashion would leave either wasted space or excess material at the junctions. There are few geometrical shapes that intersect perfectly over a surface, and of these few, the hexagon is the only one that approximates a circle. Every thin wall of wax in a hexagonal comb cell is actually a part of two cells. The midrib is not a straight

14

Most of the comb consists of worker cells (above), which are smaller than the cells of the drone (below).

sheet of wax either, for the bases of the cells intersect in pyramidal form. This is achieved by staggering the cells on either face, so that the junction of three walls on one side is at the center of a base on the other. The angular depression of the bases provides maximum strength and rigidity with a minimum of material.

Most of the comb consists of worker cells. These are used for raising worker larvae and run about five to the inch across the face. Areas of drone comb are usually found near the edges of worker combs or in storage combs built near the outside of the nest. Drones being larger than workers, their cells run about four to the inch. Either type of cell may be used for the storage of honey, but pollen is usually packed only in worker cells. Between the two groups of cells the bees construct irregular transition cells, which are used for food storage. For the raising of young queens, special cells are made when required. They are not a permanent feature of the nest, and the wax will eventually be used elsewhere when the cells have served their purpose. A queen cell is probably more primitive in its origin than those of the workers and drones. Seen in section it is not hexagonal but circular, and has an internal diameter of about five-sixteenths of an inch. It hangs vertically, as a projection from the face of a comb. The wall is quite thick, tapering off at the lower end, with a wrinkled appearance outside. When the cell is completed and the queen larva is inside, it is one inch or more in length. With its thin wax capping on the lower end molded into the structure as an inverted dome, the queen cell resembles an acorn on an oak tree.

The number of combs in a hive and their over-all dimensions depend partly on the shape and size of the cavity a colony occupies, and partly on the colony's maximum strength and its success in honey gathering. A swarm starting a new nest may make four or five combs at first, the center one perhaps ten inches wide and fourteen inches deep, the outer ones somewhat smaller. More combs can be built later, to accommodate an increased population, or to provide additional

Comb building is a major activity in the hive, especially in the spring and summer when the new brood and the nectar harvest have reached their height. The bees usually round off the lower edges of the comb in a heart shape, if the size of the cavity allows.

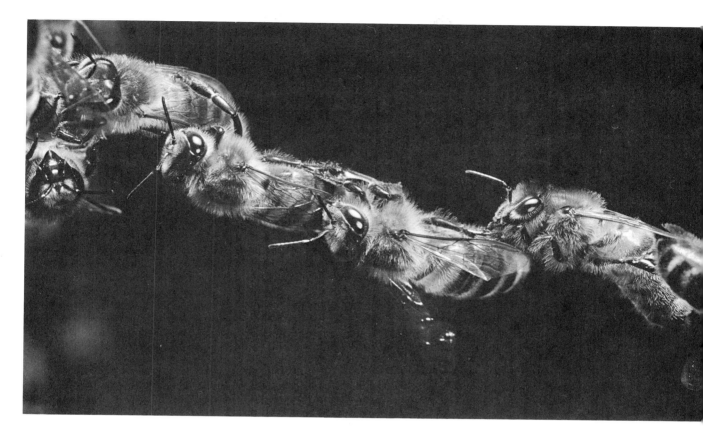

The honey-gorged waxmakers festoon themselves, clinging to one another's legs until the temperature of the cluster rises. Their food thus rapidly assimilated and their wax glands in operation, they begin building the comb.

storage space for food. A strong, well-established colony might have seven or eight combs extending down a couple of feet or more. Where the nest cavity is sufficiently narrow, the bees will always attach the upper edges of the combs to the hive sides for greater strength; the lower edges are rounded off in a sort of heart shape. In modern man-made hives the bees are induced to fill rectangular wooden frames completely with comb and honey; this facilitates their handling.

Beeswax, the comb-building material, is a gland product of young worker bees, secreted between external body plates on the underside of the abdomen. An established colony uses small quantities as required for comb repairs and cell cappings throughout the summer months, but when extensive comb building is to be done a large number of workers take part. They gorge themselves on honey and pollen, then cluster in festoonlike groups, clinging to one another's legs. The temperature of the cluster rises to 92°–97° F. as the food is rapidly assimilated. Within twenty-four hours the wax glands are in operation and the building begins, an astonishing natural process. The wax is formed as a liquid within the glands, and as it oozes out and comes into contact with the air it solidifies into tiny scales less than one-sixteenth of an inch across. These are removed from the abdomen by the hind legs and passed up to the mouth, where they are masticated as other secretions are added to them. Finally each waxmaker, working in a team and using its jaws as sculpting tools, molds its contribution precisely into the structure. Under good conditions a colony can produce several square feet of completed comb within a week. Wax production is quite costly to the bees; one pound of it, which makes about five square feet of comb, involves the consumption of at least seven pounds of honey.

The bees begin new comb by depositing a line of wax along the surface from which it will hang. More than one comb may be started simultaneously, and some natural geometry must determine the position of these center lines to produce the normal comb thickness and spacing. Very soon the line shows the angular cell bases of the midrib or septum. With instinctive precision the work continues downward, and the cell walls begin to appear. So the building proceeds, midrib ahead, with the growing cells above, until each cell is about seven-sixteenths of an inch deep on each side. The completed walls are only a few thousandths of an inch thick, but at all stages there is a thickened rim at the mouth of the cell that maintains the necessary strength there. In a vertical section through a comb the cells are seen to be not horizontal but sloping upward to the mouths; thus they are able to contain liquids. Everything about the construction of honeycomb is an example of the efficient use of material. Both lightness and strength are obtained with a substance that at first glance would seem quite unsuitable.

Newly built comb varies in color from off-white to pale yellow, with occasionally an orange tinge, according to slight differences in the chemical composition of the food consumed by the builders, or even according to the particular strain of bee. Melted down into a block, the color will be somewhat intensified, but pure beeswax is always slightly translucent. The wax becomes adulterated with age, and old comb melted down gives a much darker product, though it can be purified commercially. Wax in new comb has a pleasant honeylike odor; very soft at first, it hardens and strengthens during the next few days through the evaporation of the volatile substances that were added to it during manipulation. Subsequent varnishing of the surfaces further increases the strength. A honeycomb can last many years.

There is another material important to nest building and hive maintenance. The bees use propolis, a sticky resinous substance gathered from the buds and other parts of trees, as a varnish and glue. They also mix it with wax to fill large gaps in the hive that would otherwise expose them to weather and enemies. Some strains of bees, notably those from eastern Europe, will actually build curtains of such material to reduce the size of hive entrances before the onset of winter. Derived from the Greek, propolis means literally 'before the city.' The bees' use of it in their construction bears this meaning out.

This tenacious substance must be very difficult for the bees to handle. A forager removes it from the plant buds with its mandibles, and laboriously transfers it to the pollen baskets on its hind legs. The amount it carries is much less than a full pollen load. When the forager returns to the hive the propolis is removed by other bees, who tear it away and shred it with their jaws, for immediate use. Possibly they add gland secretions to soften it for handling. Quite often bees will gather gummy materials of human manufacture such as oil paint or varnish or coal tar, which they seem to use in the same way as propolis.

Propolis has antibiotic properties that tend to reduce mold growth in the hive and on the combs. Tradition has it that the early Italian violinmakers used propolis in their varnishes, and therein lay the secret of the wonderful tone of the instruments. But these varnishes were supplanted by those made from spirit-soluble gums from the East, such as shellac, and there seems to be no commercial use for propolis at the present time. Occasionally a small animal such as a mouse, whose body is too large for the workers to remove, will get into a hive and die there, perhaps killed by the bees. Then the whole carcass will be covered with a thick layer of propolis. This prevents putrefaction, which would be most unpleasant for the hive's inhabitants, and possibly harmful.

Life within the magnificently constructed home teems with well-organized activity. The spaces between the comb faces are packed with jostling bees, living brown seams against the pale wax. A few may be resting, but most are on the move all the time. The crowding plays an important part in the conservation of heat, which is vital to the colony. Heads are frequently being thrust into cells, for there are larvae to feed and food to be transferred to or from storage. Flashes of color are provided by the pollen-packed legs of foragers home from the fields and seeking a place to deposit their burden. Each individual has a job to do. Every worker is at any given moment a member of a group performing a specific task, and yet can readily switch to another group when colony needs demand it. There is always a colony consciousness of the hive's needs, and continual communication between individuals transmits this information. Delicate mechanisms exist whereby control of physical factors in the hive itself is possible. Most of these things will be dealt with in subsequent chapters.

The brood nest is a distinct part of the hive, but has no fixed position or size. Any of the combs may be used for the purpose, but the brood is always concentrated in one area. This provides the most efficient control of the temperature and other conditions, and facilitates the feeding of larvae in large numbers. The nest is started in the early months of the year, within the semihibernating cluster of bees, where the incubating temperature can be attained. The first eggs will be

The brood nest is a distinct part of the hive, though it is not placed in any special position, nor is it of a fixed size. After the eggs are laid in a regular pattern by the queen the tireless nurses take over the task of feeding the new brood.

laid by the queen in small patches on adjacent areas of two or three of the central combs. Subsequent expansion is three dimensional, gradually occupying more combs and a larger area of each, but still compact. The brood nest, therefore, is roughly spherical, with the combs passing through it.

Brood production at first depends on stored food, whose consumption automatically leaves room for expansion. Later, as new nectar and pollen are brought in from the fields their storage takes place outside—mainly above—the brood area. Pollen is placed immediately adjacent to the brood nest, where it will be readily available, and nectar just beyond the pollen. The contraction of the brood nest toward the end of summer will tend to be downward, leaving the stores above. Here the winter cluster will form and slowly eat its way upward in the succeeding months, until the annual rhythm of the hive has completed the full cycle.

The feeding and subsequent life history of all larvae follow a general pattern, but there are certain differences between those destined to be the workers, the drones, and the queens. In the last named, these differences are of unique importance, and will be dealt with in detail in the next chapter, on the mother bee. As workers form the bulk of the hive population, most of the following refers particularly to them.

In each case the egg in its cell hatches in three days. A little pool of food is put around it just before this occurs, so that once it breaks through the chorion that has contained it, the tiny larva may begin to feed immediately. Already considerable development has taken place: the wormlike segmentation of the body is visible, with head and mouthparts formed. However, a honeybee larva is much simpler than, say, a caterpillar. It has no need for legs or eyes, for it does not find its own food; and because a large part of its food consists of a glandular secretion from the nurses, the digestive system is relatively simple, too. Actually the main gut does not pass right through the body; the rear portion is not connected to the rest until the larva is fully fed, and waste products are retained until then.

The brood food, or bee milk, comes from the pharyngeal glands in the heads of the nurse bees, who feed liberally on pollen. Consequently the bee milk is extremely rich in proteins and certain vitamins. Because of the abundance of this food found in queen cells it is called royal jelly, and wonderful properties have been ascribed to it. There are some who maintain that small amounts of royal jelly have a rejuvenating effect on human beings and that it is beneficial in the treatment of some of our diseases. Whatever the truth of these assertions, bee milk is certainly a wonder food as far as bee larvae are concerned—their growth is prodigious. In six days of feeding a larva grows to 1,500 times its original weight. This incredible rate indicates the tremendous activity of the nurse bees. Feeding visits total about one thousand a day for each larva in the early stages, and increase to as many as three thousand in the last twenty-four hours before the cell is sealed over. Each visit lasts only a few seconds, but the German scientist Martin Lindauer calculated that together they would total about ten and one quarter bee-hours.

For the first three days all larvae are mass fed. They lie on the bases of their cells, partly immersed in a pool of food, which is constantly being replenished as they absorb it. There are slight but progressive changes in the composition of the food during this time. On the third day the worker will begin to receive raw pollen grains in its food, and is then weaned on a diet of plain honey and pollen. Moreover, the larva no longer floats in the food, but is given restricted meals at frequent intervals. At the end of six days the grub, now large and fat, fully occupies its cell and contains within itself all the material needed to form an adult bee during metamorphosis. At this stage the hive waxmakers cover the mouth of the cell with a porous capping, which shields the occupant from disturbance during the delicate processes that are to follow but still allows it to breathe. In established colonies the wax in the cappings is used over and over and becomes quite brown. Thus the areas of sealed brood are distinguished from those of sealed honey, which are always covered with new wax.

After sealing, the larva stretches lengthwise along its cell, head toward the capping, and spins itself a light cocoon, using silk from glands in its head. Then begins the great change: tissues break down and are reconstituted for the development of organs that were only rudimentary buds in the larva. The ringed segments of the body now group themselves distinctly into head, thorax, and abdomen, with the slender connecting portions that will give freedom of movement to the adult. Antennae and legs start to grow, eyes and adult mouthparts form, and the skin outgrowth on the thorax that will become the wings, begins. Internally a similar revolution is taking place: The simple gut becomes the more complex digestive system of the bee, and the elaborate gland system comes into being. Breathing and blood-circulation systems are modified, and the sting, with its associated muscle and lever system, develops. After the first two days the larva molts its final skin and is then a pupa—a soft white doll resembling a bee, but lacking the tough brown chitin that will form its external skeleton. Finally,

The metamorphosis of a worker honeybee.

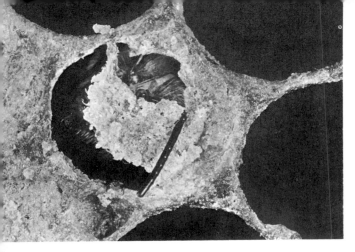
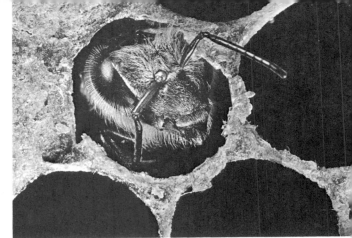

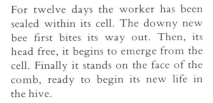

For twelve days the worker has been
sealed within its cell. The downy new
bee first bites its way out. Then, its
head free, it begins to emerge from the
cell. Finally it stands on the face of the
comb, ready to begin its new life in
the hive.

after spending twelve days sealed within its cell—twenty-one days from the time the egg was laid—the slightly downy new worker bites its way through the cell capping and climbs out onto the face of the comb. A little unsteady on its feet at first, it will be ready to begin its share of the colony's tasks within a few hours.

Optimum brood-raising temperature is 95 degrees, and this is normally maintained within one or two degrees, whatever the temperature outdoors. Most of the necessary heat is generated by the rapid metabolism of the brood itself and is conserved by the dense mass of bees over it. Away from the brood, the hive is considerably cooler; adults will continue to be active in temperature as low as 57 degrees. At the other extreme, bees of European origin tend to become distressed, as well as inactive in the field, if external shade temperatures rise above 100. Control of both temperature and moisture are two of the jobs done by a group called the house bees. They circulate the air through the nest by fanning their wings, not haphazardly, but in teams placed so as to direct the flow of air to best advantage. The number of bees taking part and the vigor of their activity will vary according to requirements. Sometimes just a few individuals will be distributed along the comb edges, with barely perceptible wing movements; but on a hot day during a honey flow many hundreds will be engaged, and the roar of their wings can be heard yards away from the hive. Then there may be two groups outside the hive entrance: one, facing outward, sends fresh air in with their vibrating wings; the other, facing inward, propels stale air out. Up on the walls inside, others will be circulating the flow.

Relative humidity can also vary greatly in the hive as a whole. It will, of course, tend to be highest in wet weather, but in the brood area it has been shown to be fairly constant, somewhere between 35 and 45 percent. The normal digestive process involving the combustion of sugar produces a lot of water vapor, but any excess is removed by the ventilation activity. In hot dry weather the problem may be reversed. It then becomes necessary to restrict the loss of moisture from the larvae and their food and still keep the temperature at its proper level. Here the wonderful instincts of the bee enable it to apply principles of physics only recently understood by man. Water is brought into the hive and spread out in small amounts on the dimpled surfaces of wax and on hive parts, so that it will evaporate into the airstream created by the house bees. This evaporation takes heat from the air, and at the same time the added vapor raises its humidity so that normal conditions can be maintained. It is a thoroughly efficient system of air conditioning.

Within the hive the bee has learned not only to organize its corporate life to a high level of efficiency, but also to exercise remarkable control over its environment. The senses, skills, and behavior patterns that it has evolved for its field activities are of a very high order too.

3. the mother bee

Insect societies are matriarchal; the males do no share of the work and appear to wield no influence other than indirectly through the mating act. Family life is centered around the egg-laying females; with the honeybee, it is a single female. The queen is indispensable. She alone lays the eggs that produce successive generations of workers; and although their lives are measured in weeks, she herself may live several years. She is the source of life to the hive, and even more; for, as we shall see later, the consciousness of her presence is the cohesive force that binds the colony together and keeps this complex organization running smoothly.

Finding a queen among her many offspring might seem an impossible task, but skill comes with practice. She is, after all, distinguishable from her subjects by her length and the shape of her abdomen. Her wings, although slightly longer than those of a worker, look shorter in relation to her longer body, and her smooth long legs look brighter. The way she walks, too, is quite distinctive to the trained eye, and unless she is violently disturbed, her gentle passage across the combs has all the grace that her royal title suggests. Wherever she goes, a group of workers nearby will turn toward her, ready to act as attendants. She is fed and cleaned by them as she performs her duties. In a glass-sided observation hive you sometimes see workers form an almost perfect circle, heads turned in toward the queen, who occupies a clear space in the center.

The queen is in effect an egg-laying machine. Her capacity to produce eggs in large numbers over long periods is fundamental to bee life. She is ideally equipped for the purpose: most of her long abdomen is occupied by a pair of elaborate ovaries, containing, when she is in full lay, many hundreds of eggs in successive stages of development. In achieving this specialized function, the queen has lost many of the ancestral attributes that persist in her sterile daughters. Unlike the queen bumblebee, for instance, the queen honeybee is unable to gather food, build comb, or even help feed her offspring. She is as completely dependent upon the workers as the whole colony is upon her. The long tongue and other mouthparts of bee workers enable them to extract nectar from flowers; the queen's tongue has become shortened, and other parts of the mouth are simplified. She is normally fed mouth to mouth by workers, although she can take food from the comb cells when necessary. The gland systems in the head and thorax of a worker

The queen is constantly surrounded by workers. They turn toward her, tending to her needs as she goes among them.

are elaborate; in the queen they are either atrophied or modified for other purposes. Her legs, too, are bereft of the pollen-gathering and wax-handling tools of the worker.

Eggs are laid singly in the comb cells, which have been cleaned and prepared by young workers. First the queen puts her head down inside the cell to inspect it, rejecting any that are unsuitable; then, moving forward and grasping the edges of adjacent cells with her feet, she arches her back and inserts her abdomen right down to the base of the cell. Here she lays the egg, one end of which attaches itself to the cell by a sticky secretion. Because the egg stands almost vertically from the cell base, and is white and nearly one-sixteenth of an inch long, it is quite visible. The routine is truly machinelike: one egg laid every few seconds, with intervals for feeding and grooming, twenty-four hours a day, every day through the spring and summer. It is not unknown for a queen to lay 2,000 eggs a day at her peak, a total product greater than her own weight. This represents an extraordinary rate of metabolism, even allowing for her being fed a processed food—the bee milk, or royal jelly.

She fills the central area of a comb first, then works concentrically outward to the limit of the brood nest. The next comb is treated similarly, so not only is the queen's time used efficiently, but also that of the workers who must subsequently tend the larvae. They will have groups of the same age close together. The queen gets her real rest in the late fall, when laying usually ceases for some weeks, and sometimes for several months.

The biological miracle by which honeybees are able to create new queens at will is not only a necessary part of colony reproduction, but a tremendously important factor in the continuity of its existence as well. The impulse to start

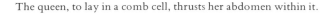

The queen, to lay in a comb cell, thrusts her abdomen within it.

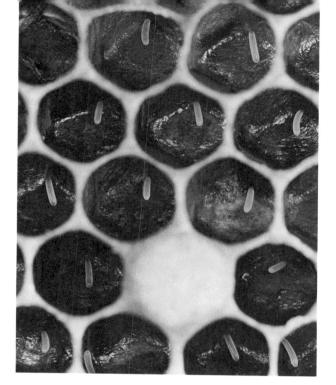

The eggs are laid singly, one in each cell.

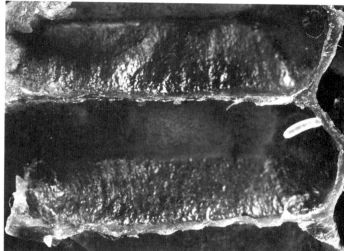

The egg is attached to the base of the cell by a sticky secretion.

queen raising can come from any one of three sets of circumstances. One is when the colony has reached its peak of population and prosperity and is ready for reproduction. This is known as the swarming impulse. A second occurs when the existing mother is beginning to fail, because of old age or physical defect, and needs to be replaced. Such replacement is called supersedure. And third, there is the emergency impulse, arising with the sudden loss of the mother bee, who may suffer a physical breakdown or be killed accidentally. Part of a colony, including the queen, might be lost through severe storm damage to its hive or an attack by insect-eating birds or rodents. A hungry bear could create the same situation. Should the disaster occur between April and September in the temperate zones, the colony would have a fair chance of survival; but a young queen produced in the winter could not mate, for there are no drones available then, and the colony would be doomed.

When queens are produced under the swarming impulse, the initial procedure differs from that under supersedure or the emergency impulse. The eggs are laid in special preconstructed queen cells and treated as potential queens right from the start. As summer approaches, any prosperous colony will build on the lower, or side, edges of its brood combs a few round inverted wax cells known as queen cups. If the urge to swarm arises, eggs will be laid in three, four, or maybe a dozen or more of these. Observation suggests that a queen does not willingly leave the ordinary comb cells to lay eggs in the queen cups, but appears to be forced by her attendants. She is the tool, not the instigator, of the colony's destiny.

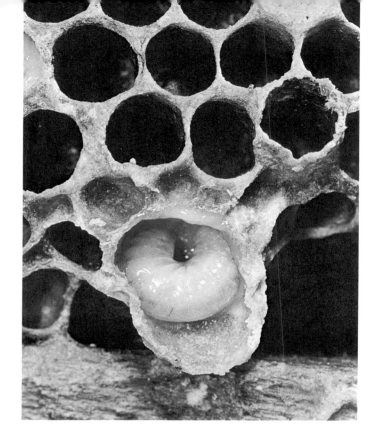

A fully grown larva within the queen cell.

These eggs hatch in the ordinary way, and as the larvae grow the cells are extended downward to become completed queen cells.

In both supersedure and emergency queen raising, the cell is constructed around an existing larva in a worker cell on the face of a brood comb. The mouth of the cell is enlarged, and building proceeds outward and downward until it looks the same as a swarm cell, and the larva inside has assumed the vertical position. The vital factor in the selection of a worker larva to be raised as a queen is its age: the larva must be not yet weaned, less than three days old. The remainder of its larval life is now almost a matter of hours, and yet the treatment it receives during that time determines not only changes in its physique, but also a vastly different future.

A queen larva continues to be fed on the secreted bee milk throughout its life, and in contrast to the weaned workers, the queen larva receives it in abundant quantities. There is always a white mass of it in the cell, more than the larva needs, so that a surplus usually remains when the full-grown virgin emerges after pupation. Though this rich and lavish feeding is a major factor in the development of a queen, it is not the whole story.

A very young larva taken from a preconstructed queen cell shows greater development of its rudimentary ovaries than one of the same age taken from a worker cell. When a worker larva is selected to be changed into a queen, it soon starts a similar development, which proceeds rapidly. Unless it was getting close to its weaning period when selected, this larva has a good chance of becoming as well-developed a queen as any other. Almost certainly involved are one or more hormones—those complex chemical substances that, in minute quantities, control the growth and function of living things. Perhaps the nurses provide a hormone that promotes the sexual development of the queen while inhibiting the growth of certain other organs that are developed in the worker; or perhaps workers may get a hormone that inhibits their sexual function. The mystery is still to be solved.

Scientists have had success in the raising of worker larvae, by hand, on food taken from normal brood cells, but attempts to raise queens in this fashion have so far produced only freaks that died before pupation. However, the knowledge we have now is of very great value to the beekeeper. Colonies can be induced to rear queens at the beekeeper's convenience, so that he may either increase his stock or replace old ones before they begin to fail.

The sealing of a queen cell takes place after only five and a half days of feeding. This is half a day less than with a worker; but, unlike the worker, the queen larva still has plenty of food in the cell and probably continues to feed a few more hours after sealing and before spinning a cocoon. It does seem strange that the larger insect, the true female, should also pass through metamorphosis in less time than a worker, but it is so. A young queen will emerge from her

The metamorphosis of a queen is much more rapid than that of a worker or drone. The cell is sealed after $5\frac{1}{2}$ days of feeding; the queen will emerge from the egg 16 days after it was laid.

The struggle of rival queens means death for one of them. The fighting skirmish; one gains the advantage; the fatal thrust.

cell on the sixteenth day after the egg was laid, five days sooner than a worker.

Except occasionally during supersedure, it is rare for a colony to raise just one queen at a given time, even though one is all that is required; nature does not take risks in these matters. Should two virgins emerge from their cells at about the same time, they will seek out each other and fight until one receives a fatal sting. The victor is always uninjured, for the struggle involves getting into a position from which one fatal thrust can be made, generally through the soft integument between the overlapping plates of the abdomen. Death to the loser is swift, and the body is soon unceremoniously thrown out by the workers, who play no part in the battle. More often one virgin appears before the others and immediately seeks to destroy her rivals by attacking them in their cells. She will tear down the side of a cell with her mandibles, insert her sting, and kill her helpless sister within. Then the workers enlarge the hole and drag out the corpse.

A virgin queen, conscious of the presence of others in the hive, will make a 'zeep-zeep' noise, known as piping, sometimes loud enough to be detected by human ears several yards from the hive. The intermittent sound, made while the insect squats low on the comb with trembling wings, is probably caused solely by the wing vibration; but some think that air passing over the spiracles in the abdomen is responsible. Piping is most frequently heard at swarming time. After the prime swarm has left, some strong colonies will prepare to send out a second or even a third swarm. These are called afterswarms, or casts. In this case the bees will not allow the first virgin to kill the others, who will be kept imprisoned in their cells until she has left with the cast. This is done by preventing them from biting through the cappings of their cells. The clear shrill piping of the free queen can now be heard against the more muffled tones of the prisoners. Curiously, during supersedure there is no such rivalry between a young queen and the old mother she is to replace.

Given fine weather, a young queen will start making prenuptial flights when she is two or three days old, and mating may take place after the fifth day. She is very cautious at first, staying close to the hive as she circles it, and returning in a few minutes. With each flight she is further gaining the use of her wings; and succeeding flight circles grow ever wider, for she must learn the hive's precise position in relation to the surrounding area. She would be killed instantly if she accidentally entered the wrong one after mating. The majority of queens mate between the fifth and tenth days, and they must do so within three weeks or their physical capacity to mate is lost. Some queens will begin to lay about forty-eight hours after mating, but others may not start for several days. Bad weather following the mating may delay egg laying for a couple of weeks. Once a queen has mated and started to lay, it is unlikely that she will ever leave the hive again, except with a swarm. The implications of this are astounding. Over a period of perhaps two or three years a queen will lay several hundred thousand worker eggs, each one fertilized by a male sperm, and yet she has but a single mating period in early life. Clearly there must be some unusual arrangement to insure the fertilization of such a huge number of eggs over this long a period.

Within the abdomen of a queen, adjacent to the tube that carries the eggs down from the ovaries, is a spherical organ called a spermatheca. Sperms, received from drones during mating, make their way to this storage chamber, from which they can be released to fertilize eggs as they travel down the tube to be laid. It is inconceivable that the microscopic sperms are released one at a time, although only one is required for each egg. The sperms are thought to be dispersed in small batches, with one entering the micropyle of each worker egg by chemical attraction. The number of sperms held in the spermatheca is enormous; and by some delicate process they are kept alive, in cold storage, as it were, until wanted. Now that we know a little more about the mating period of queen bees, the whole thing is more credible.

Until quite recently it was thought that a queen mated with one drone only, but here and there observers had reported seeing a queen mate twice, either on the same day or on two successive days. The perfection of a technique for the artificial insemination of queen bees showed that the spermatheca of a fully mated queen contains more sperms than a single drone could provide; several drones had to be used each time. This inspired further investigations into natural mating. Dr. J. Woyke, a Polish scientist, performed a series of experiments, first in Poland and later in the United States, involving the extensive observation of many hundreds of queens. Each one was watched closely during its mating period

The photomicrograph of a section shows the development of eggs within the ovary. Every worker egg, of which the queen will lay several hundred thousand during her life, will be fertilized by a male sperm; yet the queen has but one brief mating period.

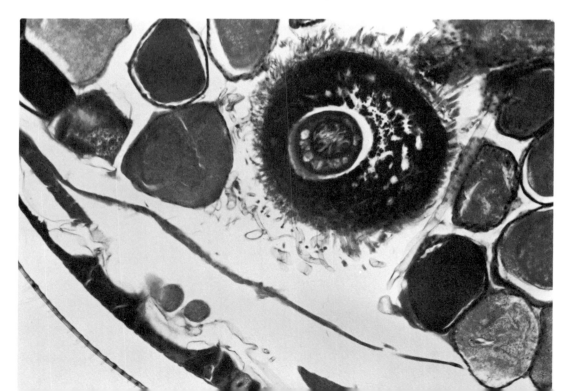

and subsequently dissected to count the sperms stored in the spermatheca. The results proved that normally at least five drones were involved in the matings of a single queen, sometimes more than double that number, with the average being more than seven. Many complete matings took place on a single half-hour flight, but some queens made a second and even a third flight, either on the same day or on succeeding days. So the offspring of one individual female have a number of different fathers. Beekeepers have often noticed two groups of different-colored workers in the same hive when more than one strain of bee is kept in the apiary.

A young queen chooses the middle part of a fine day in which to make a mating flight, and soon has a concourse of drones following her. They definitely seem to hunt in packs. Some observers believe that there are certain spots in a district to which young queens fly and where drones congregate, sometimes called mating markets. Given good weather conditions, very few queens fail to mate successfully. The scent from the body of a nubile queen can attract drones from a considerable distance, often a mile or more. On a mating flight the drones gather and follow her in a formation that resembles the tail of a comet; sometimes the whole entourage sweeps close to the ground, and then wings high out of sight. The mass zigzags in a manner that makes detailed observation difficult, but the act does take place on the wing. The pair occasionally fall to the ground afterward. But usually, once the queen's vaginal chamber is open and the first drone has mounted her, others do so in quick succession. A drone leaves a plug of mucus in the chamber, which prevents the semen from running out before the sperms have traveled to the spermatheca. In the successive matings, the plug left by one drone is automatically removed by the next act of copulation. The final plug is removed from the queen's body by workers, after she has returned to the hive. This 'mating sign' on the queen as she returns home is well known to observant beekeepers.

While she is a virgin the young queen appears to receive little notice from the workers in a hive, although they are conscious of her presence and become somewhat disturbed if she is removed. There is often some excitement at the hive entrance when she is setting out on her mating flight; the bees seem to be almost pushing her out. Once she returns from a successful venture she becomes a focus of attention, being frequently fed and groomed. Very soon the developing eggs in the ovaries increase the length of her abdomen. Within a few days the slim and active maid becomes a stately matron, ready to do her life's work.

A source of life, the queen is also a prime source of well-being to the bees. If by some mischance a colony is suddenly deprived of its queen, it will show signs of obvious distress within a matter of minutes. Numbers of bees begin to scurry to and fro on the inside and up and down the outside of the hive in search of her, and a loud buzzing of wings proclaims that all is not well. Should she not return, emergency queen cells will be started within a few hours. After that, the initial excitement abates, but the colony remains alert and uneasy, with the normal rhythm of work disorganized, until a new queen is present.

One of the most fascinating studies of recent years concerns the role of the queen in maintaining the emotional equilibrium of the colony, and the control of its instinct to raise other queens. It has been noticed that attendant bees frequently lick the body of the queen as she goes about her duties, far more frequently than seems necessary for mere cleaning purposes, and that these bees then offer their tongues to others near by, who are eager to reciprocate. Do the attendants get from the queen's body some substance that gives them a sense of satisfaction, and then pass some of it on to their fellows? Dr. Colin Butler, of Rothamsted Experimental Station, England, set out to investigate this in a series of clever experiments. He found that bees, in the presence of a caged queen whom they could feed but not lick, soon began to build some queen cells over young worker larvae, exactly as a queenless colony would do. But if the queen was so caged that she could be licked as well as fed, then queen cells were not started, even though the caging prevented her from laying. Dr. Butler concluded that there must be a chemical 'queen substance,' as he called it, that is passed from bee to bee round the colony, and that it has a profound effect on the colony's behavior. Eventually he found the substance originates in the mandibular glands in the queen's mouth. It has since been synthesized by chemists, and may some day prove to be of value to beekeepers in the management of their colonies. It appears that the colony always has the latent urge to raise queens—after all, they are the true females—but the queen substance acts as an inhibitor. While the workers are receiving an adequate quantity of it no queen cells will be started, but if for any reason the supply fails, queen-raising operations begin. Presumably an old queen reaches a stage when she is unable to produce enough of the substance. Steps are then taken to supersede her, even in her presence. The accidental loss of a queen means a sudden cutoff of the supply and consequent excitement. At swarming time, the queen must pass through a phase when her production of the substance is temporarily reduced, or the amount she has to give is insufficient for the then very large population. We still have much to learn about the subject.

Dr. Butler later found that the queen-cell-inhibiting substance was not the only one both special to queens and important to the colony. There is at least one other, also glandular in origin, that is needed to keep the bees contented and the hive's rhythm normal. It is known that a queen bee emits an odor that is recognizable to worker bees anywhere. They will always respond to the presence of a queen, without necessarily making any direct contact. A whole new field of research has been opened up, for it appears that all social animals, humans included, may produce subtle chemical substances that act between individuals in the mass and tend to coordinate and balance the organized existence. Within the living individual the hormones perform such functions internally; scientists have given the name 'pheromones' to these substances that act externally.

4. drones

During the warmest hours of summer days, amid the hum of countless worker bees flying about their business, we may hear around the hive the deep loud buzzing of drones in apparently aimless flight. 'The lazy yawning drone,' as Shakespeare called him, has always been the symbol of idleness, a loafer inside the hive and a noisy swaggerer without.

How wrong we are when we ascribe human motives to creatures so utterly different from ourselves. The truth is that drones are not merely male bees; they are also a specialized caste, as single in function as a queen is—more so, in fact, for drones do not appear to have any special effect on colony well-being. They gather no pollen or nectar from the flowers because they possess neither the organs nor the senses to do so. They build no comb, for they have no wax glands, and their mandibles are unfitted to work this material. And they are completely defenseless, for nature has denied them a sting. But the drone is a powerful flyer and an inveterate wanderer, with exceptionally large eyes and acute organs of scent that enable him to seek out young queens that are ready for mating. His whole being is devoted to this function—and death his only reward for final success.

The much-maligned drone has a function in the hive as specialized as that of the mother bee. His life work is to mate with a queen.

The drone's enormous compound eyes, whose 8,500 facets give him nearly 360-degree vision, help him seek out young queens that are ready for mating.

This burly member of the colony is not quite so long as a queen in full lay, but is definitely heavier. The broad abdomen is somewhat square at the end, with a distinctive fringe of hair. The head and antennae are larger than those of either worker or queen, and the huge compound eyes almost meet on the face and extend well around to the rear of the head. About 8,500 facets in each make the angle of vision practically 360 degrees. Undoubtedly the drone's sight enables him to detect young queens more readily, but compound eyes are not good at analyzing detail. On a mating flight he has a tendency to chase anything that moves across his field of vision within a few yards.

In the hive, drones tend to gather in groups in areas of comb that are on the fringes of the brood nest—in the warmth, but out of the workers' way. They move slowly, even if the hive is disturbed, and are disinclined to take wing other than in the middle hours of warm days. A minimum temperature of 60 seems necessary for drones to fly at all, and mating flights require 68 degrees or more. The first flights of a drone, like those of queen and worker, are for orientation purposes; and in casual flight there is no tendency to gather in groups, as is the case when mating.

A colony carries no drones during the winter months; this would use up precious food stores to no purpose, for young queens are raised only in the summer. Drone raising is begun in the spring, several weeks before any new queens are likely to appear, for it takes longer to produce sexually mature drones than it does queens. As the colony expands, its queen will begin to lay eggs in the drone comb and continue to do so in modest numbers until summer is on the wane or a severe food shortage occurs. The eggs placed in drone cells always produce male bees, just as those placed in worker cells develop into females. The queen can switch from one type of cell to the other and seems never to make a mistake, unless she is old or physically abnormal. The reason for her accuracy is another mystery that is not yet solved.

The German-born Reverend Johann Dzierzon—in 1845 in Poland—was the first to put forth the theory of parthenogenesis in respect to drones. It has since been abundantly proved. The drone comes from an unfertilized egg; every fertilized egg produces a female. The worker bee, like most other living things, inherits its characteristics from both a father and a mother, through fertilization of the egg by a male sperm. The drone, having no father, inherits characteristics from the mother only. Parthenogenesis—reproduction without male fertilization —occurs in different forms in a number of insects and some plants. Some species of aphids have no males at all. Others, like the common greenfly, produce a number of generations of females in this way, then have a season in which normal males and females occur, and mating takes place between them.

That a queen bee can control the fertilization of her eggs just before they are laid, and then put each kind in the appropriate cells is truly remarkable. It suggests free will, although insects do not possess this human attribute. For some eggs, passing down the oviduct, to receive sperms and others none through choice, would require a mechanism of very fine control, which has yet to be discovered. One theory is that every egg carries sperms when laid, but that fertilization does not take place until after the egg is in the cell. Then workers supposedly remove the sperms from the eggs in the drone cells before fertilization occurs. This presupposes some fine discrimination and timing. Practical experiments make this possibility seem most unlikely. A more probable explanation is that contact with a drone cell by a queen induces in her a reflex action through which a chemical secretion from her organs inhibits the fertilization of the egg about to be laid. A queen who has failed to mate can lay drone eggs, and an old one whose supply of sperms has run out will continue to do so. In both cases worker cells may be used, and combs get spoiled when the workers have to enlarge the cells to accommodate the growing male grubs.

When a colony has been queenless for three weeks or more and has no young larvae from which a new queen can be raised, some worker bees will then develop the capacity to lay a few eggs. Possibly because there is no brood to feed, the workers consume the brood food themselves, and the extra nourishment causes their ovaries to develop. However, the absence of the queen substance may bring about the change. The eggs are laid haphazardly in worker cells, often several in one cell. Because a worker is unable to mate, the eggs are unfertilized; and those that do hatch become undersized drones of doubtful potency. Such a colony is practically always doomed, at least in nature. A beekeeper, however, can often save his stricken family by introducing a queen to them from elsewhere.

The ordinary drone larva is fed on bee milk for the first three days, as the females are. Like the worker, it is weaned on a honey and pollen diet, but it is fed for seven days instead of six. Drone larvae stay longer in the sealed cells; in all, it takes twenty-four days to produce a drone. In addition to their size, drone cells have another distinguishing feature: the cappings are domed instead of almost flat. Once the young drone emerges he solicits food from the workers, a habit he continues even when he is able to feed direct from the comb cells. It takes another two weeks for him to reach maturity, although orientation flights are made well before that time.

Drones are accepted in any hive, and there is a tendency for them to drift during their period of potency. A beekeeper who has two distinctively different strains of bees in one apiary will see drones of both strains in each hive. Scientists have found marked drones as far as seven miles from their birthplace, a journey certainly not made in a single flight. Thus nature insures the crossbreeding that maintains the vigor of the species.

The drone's genitalia lie folded within the abdomen until immediately before the sex act. Then they are rapidly and completely everted to a position outside, a movement that is not reversible. A drone mounts the back of a queen while both are in flight, and copulation usually takes place very quickly. Observers have

The drone brood are almost always placed at the outer edges of the comb. The cells are larger than worker cells, and their cappings are domed.

reported hearing an audible snap as the two came together, probably due to the rapid eversion of the male genital organs. Immediately afterward the drone falls dead or dying to the ground. Occasionally the two fly together for a distance, the drone's powerful wings carrying the queen, before the act is consummated. Eversion of the genitalia may take place with a number of drones who do not succeed in mounting the queen, and indeed they sometimes die in this way when excited by other causes.

The number of young queens produced in a season is relatively small; some colonies may rear none at all. Even allowing for several drones to mate each queen, it is obvious that the vast majority never fulfill their life purpose. For the drone who does not die in the mating act, the life span is no longer than two months.

So for some, the end is sudden; others that were born in the spring die of old age before the season is over. For the rest, the end is ignominious. When the last of the great summer nectar flows is finished, when days are getting shorter and nights cooler, the bees know instinctively that no more queens are going to be raised, and therefore drones no longer are needed. Preparations for winter begin. The hitherto pampered males are almost overnight turned upon by their sisters. They are refused food handouts and prevented from helping themselves. Weak from starvation, they are driven outside the hive to die and become food for birds or toads. The end of a season may find a heap of the unfortunate drones on the ground in front of the hive.

When the drones are no longer needed they are unceremoniously turned out of the nest. This evicted drone lies stiff and dead outside the hive that once welcomed him.

5. workers

Worker—no other name could be given to those members of the community that perform every task, except egg laying and mating, within and without the hive. Mistress of all trades, adaptable, persistent, and endowed with self-sacrificing loyalty, the individual worker is a humble servant; collectively the workers are sovereign. They control the destiny of the superorganism, and it is their instincts and their reactions to changing circumstances that regulate the colony's behavior and take it through its annual rhythm. Paradoxically, this sterile sisterhood also initiates and directs its reproduction.

The efficient and harmonious working of the bee colony has excited naturalists and philosophers from earliest times. Aristotle, in ancient Greece, suggested that some organized division of labor must exist, but the subject remained entirely a matter for speculation until recent years. Many, who tended to use the human parallel, thought each worker followed some definite trade throughout its life and that all worked under the direction of the queen. Others, from observation, were sure the bees changed jobs from time to time, and that there must be some regulation according to the needs of the colony. The first comprehensive study of this problem was made by the German scientist Dr. G. A. Rösch during the years 1925–1930, and his conclusions laid the foundation of our present understanding.

Like others, Dr. Rösch had wondered whether the age of the bee was a factor in the division of labor. So, using a large observation hive, he designed his experiments to test this possibility. Each day he marked successive groups of emerging bees by putting spots of paint on their backs. By using several colors in various dot combinations, he could determine not only the age of any individual that was under observation, but also if particular hive duties were being performed by bees of one age group. His results showed that the general pattern of a worker's life was to perform a sequence of duties that were determined by a combination of its age and the development of certain glands.

Briefly, the newly emerged bee spends a few days on the brood combs cleaning out vacated cells, and during that time it consumes large amounts of pollen from the hive stores. This stimulates the development of its brood-food glands so that it may then become a nurse bee, feeding the larvae bee milk. After

Forager, nectar-gatherer, nurse and house bee, guardian of the hive, the worker is the heart of the colony.

the bee spends a week or so as a nurse, these glands deteriorate; but by then the wax glands are readily stimulated, and the worker is undergoing transition to become a house bee. The many duties in this stage, which do not follow a strict sequence, continue until the bee is about three weeks old. It now enters the final phase of its life, as a field bee, or forager, with its wonderful aptitudes for finding and gathering the food needed by the colony.

These times apply to only a normal colony during the summer months, when the worker's total life is about six weeks. Some of the stages may be greatly extended at other seasons, when activity is less intense; and in abnormal circumstances, such as a period of queenlessness, many individuals will bypass some duties altogether. Rösch realized that the pattern was not absolutely rigid but adaptable to circumstances.

Further work by other scientists has confirmed the basic truth of his conceptions, but there is even more flexibility than was at first thought. For instance, under emergency conditions even five-day-old bees may become foragers, and conversely, old bees may raise brood and build comb. Either may be much less efficient at these jobs than bees of normal age, but a colony that has suffered some disaster may thus be saved from extinction.

The age of a bee, then, is not entirely a matter of time, but is related to certain of its bodily functions and the rate and extent of their use. Under two extreme sets of conditions, workers may live for six months or die of old age in six weeks. The critical stage is that of the nurse bee and the use of its brood-food glands. These are a part of a complex salivary system situated in the front of the head, and consist of a group of berry-shaped bodies, and two long ducts, all folded into a compact mass. The ducts open onto the back of the tongue, and the product flows forward in the act of feeding a larva or a queen.

A young bee when three days old will be ready to start nursing larvae; and the amount of work it does will depend on the number of larvae to be fed and on how many nurses are available at the time. If the demand is high, as in late spring, then every nurse bee will be fully employed and will itself go on feeding rapidly in order to produce more brood food, until the glands degenerate. Then it must transfer to other work. Even with little brood to feed, the glands remain active for many weeks, and the life of the individual is thereby extended. A worker born in early October develops its pharyngeal glands in the usual way, but may not use them until, say, the following February. It has lived that long because physiologically it has remained a young bee.

The natural transition for the nurse bee is to become a waxmaker, for those glands now become operative. From feeding the brood it is a logical step to capping the cells. Then there are comb repairs and any new construction that may be required. In a well-established colony the full waxmaking capacity of the bees may not be used, or it may be deferred until a heavy income of nectar makes additional comb necessary. To some extent wax production is involuntary. When a colony is receiving food at a rapid pace and needs no additional comb for its storage, many little white wax flakes from the bees' bodies may be deposited on the floor of the hive.

A house bee cleans the surface of
the hive with its tongue.

House bees do all the hive cleaning, carrying or propelling the debris to the entrance and pushing it outside. The larger pieces, particularly bees that have died in the hive, or intruding insects that have been killed, will be picked up by flying members of the colony and dropped many yards away from the hive. Hundreds of old workers die every day during the summer, yet it is extraordinary how few dead ones are seen outside the hive. Most old foragers die at work in the fields, but those that die in the hive are removed, so their bodies do not accumulate in or around the home. The manipulation and storage of food is also the duty of the house bees. They relieve foragers of their loads of nectar, and finally pack the pollen after it has been deposited in the cells of the combs. In addition, propolising the holes and cracks in the hive structure, varnishing, ventilating the hive, are all jobs performed by the house bees.

Very young bees are disinclined to sting, and full development of the poison glands does not take place until the bees are reaching the field stage. House bees do not undertake guard duty until they have the real power to keep intruders away. Once a colony has become alerted, however, many foragers will take part in this activity. Their potency in this respect remains with them until the end.

The regular guards are stationed at or near the hive entrance or on the lower edges of the combs. These give the alarm when they sense a possible enemy; a distinctively pitched buzz of the wings is transmitted to other bees near by, who are instantly alerted. Should a guard become very agitated during its investigation of an intruder, its sting will begin to protrude and a tiny drop of venom will appear on the end. The pungent odor of the venom soon spreads through the hive; the normal steady hum changes to a strident buzz, and many bees are ready to do instant battle. The bee's actual use of its sting releases more odor and increases the hive's militant mood.

The temperament of individual colonies varies considerably, as indeed it does with other animals. Some strains are worse-tempered than others, but all are more readily aroused when times are hard. When the weather is fine and nectar is pouring into the hive, almost any liberties may be taken; but in the fall, when flowers become scarce and the winter stores have to be protected, tempers are likely to be short and the guards very active. Once a colony has been thoroughly alerted it may remain so for as long as twenty-four hours; then woe betide the innocent passer-by who gets a bit too close to the hive entrance!

A worker will be about ten days old when it makes its first venture into the outside world. Another ten may pass before the bee does any actual field work. Its first sorties are orientation flights, similar to those made by the queen and the drones. Perhaps the initial urge comes from a need to empty the bowel of waste matter, an act that normally takes place on the wing. Retention over a period of bad weather is quite possible, and no healthy worker ever soils the inside of the hive except in very prolonged winter conditions. In these play flights, as the bee-keeper calls them, large groups of young bees will take part at one time. Swinging

The worker is about ten days old when it leaves the hive on its first flight.

backward and forward in front of the entrance, or making small circles around the hive, they are obviously learning to locate its position. They always choose a warm half hour or so in the middle of the day for this, and their playful maneuvers, so different from the purposeful flight of their older sisters, are a joy to watch.

Once the worker starts to make regular trips to the fields it gives up household tasks and enters the final phase of its life. Now it has developed to the full its marvelous navigational sense and the ability to communicate information about food sources to its fellows. In this second half of its existence, the worker will fly many miles in seeking and bringing home the food and other materials necessary for the colony's existence. Gradually its body becomes more shiny as the hair covering wears off, the wings get ragged, and finally comes the flight from which it fails to return.

The material requirements of the colony are water, pollen, nectar, and propolis, and the foragers are marshaled to meet them. The division of labor among the force is no longer on strictly physiological grounds. It is very flexible and created by changing factors, which include the demands of the nurse and house bees, the instinct to gather food for storage, and the current availability of

Large amounts of water are needed to dilute the food for the brood, so a great many foragers are recruited as water carriers.

nectar and pollen. There are times, even in midsummer, when very little of either of these is available. Then large numbers of foragers may stay at home, hanging in clusters below the combs or congregating in the storage areas.

The behavior of a small proportion of bees tends to be individual and less subject to the changing influences that affect the others. Some of these may start off gathering pollen or nectar and make it their lifework. Other, perhaps more important, individuals seem to have no disposition to remain at one job. They are wanderers, who in their searchings render valuable service by locating new food sources that the others will exploit to the full.

A young forager may well start as a water carrier. Water is necessary for all members of the colony, but nurse bees use large quantities of it to dilute food for the young, especially if they are working with stored honey rather than new nectar. Water carrying fluctuates noticeably according to demand. In early spring when brood raising increases rapidly the gatherers will be particularly busy. A strong colony may use up to one pint a day. Water is carried in the crop, or honey sac, in the same way as nectar, but is not stored in the combs. House bees take it from the foragers, and some of the former act as tankers, giving it to others as required. After a rain, bees can be seen drinking from grass or tree leaves near the hive, but each colony will have its own favorite drinking place. It is likely to be on the muddy edge of a stream or pool, close to the hive where possible, and exposed to the sun so the water can get warm. Water carrying is a risky occupation in the early days of the year. A bee may fly through a cold-air zone that lowers its body temperature to the point where the bee loses mobility and never regains it. Doubtless a number of bees are lost in this way, but colony welfare demands that risks be taken.

Foragers gather nectar and pollen for the hive whenever conditions permit. Most bees go out on a succession of trips, as either pollen collectors or nectar collectors, and return home with full loads of one or the other. But again there are the few independent individuals who may gather some of each on a single journey. There are more of these individuals in times of scarcity when more searching has to be done and any small amount of food is welcome. The proportion of pollen gatherers to nectar gatherers is regulated partly by the availability of the respective substances, and partly by the demand for pollen in the brood nest; but when nectar is abundant most of the foragers turn to its collection.

Although the mouthparts of all insects conform to the same general plan, there are wide variations to suit the great range of feeding habits. The proboscis of the worker bee has special adaptations for collecting nectar. In the center is a long, slender tongue, which can be extended and contracted lengthwise. When not in use, it and the associated parts are carried curled beneath the mouth. The tongue has many hairs, terminates in a spoon-shaped lobe, and when fully extended it protrudes about three-sixteenths of an inch beyond the jaws, or mandibles. Four other parts, in two pairs and having sense organs, called the

The worker is especially equipped to gather nectar. Using its long, slender tongue with a spoon-shaped end, it can extract the nectar from the heart of a flower.

labial palpi and galeae, can enclose the tongue to form a tube around it. At work on a liquid the tongue does a rapid up-and-down movement inside the tube, while the spoon end exerts a lapping motion to propel the liquid upward. Within the head there is a muscular sac that acts as a sucking pump to continue the flow into the alimentary canal.

The forager needs storage space within its body to take home the sweet nectar, and a ready means to discharge the load when it gets there. From the mouth the liquid passes through the thorax along a narrow tube into the honey sac at the beginning of the abdomen. This organ corresponds to the normal insect crop, and has the usual valve called the proventriculus, separating it from the stomach. The proventriculus of the honeybee prevents the passage of nectar into the digestive system proper, unless the bee needs some of it for her own nourishment. It has another remarkable function: By a pulsating action of the four flaps of the valve nearly all the grains of pollen that have accidentally collected in the nectar are separated from it and are retained when the load is discharged. Subsequently they are delivered into the stomach. The final adaptation of the whole system is a reversing mechanism for the sucking pump. In this way the contents of the honey sac are readily regurgitated. A full load is about seventy milligrams, 85 per cent of the bee's normal weight. The homecoming forager does not discharge nectar directly into a comb cell; it is always offered to other bees. Food sharing is a social habit of importance in communication and colony cohesion. Most of the load is transferred to the house bees, who have the job of converting it into honey and arranging for the storage.

The conversion of nectar into honey involves two major processes: concentration by the removal of water, and a chemical change of the sugars. The nectar when gathered contains three different sugars—sucrose, glucose, and fructose—in varying proportions, but sucrose always forms the major part. Glucose and fructose are simple sugars, monosaccharides, that are readily assimiliated into the bloodstream of an animal. Sucrose is a disaccharide that has to be broken down by some digestive process before it can be assimilated. The house bees add a digestive enzyme, sucrase, to the nectar while they are processing it, and that splits the sucrose into glucose and fructose. Honey, then, is really a predigested food, demanding the minimum of energy from the wintering bees for its assimilation. And incidentally, honey is also readily absorbed into the human digestive system.

The average sugar content of nectar is about 40 percent; in ripe honey it is 80 percent. The difference represents the amount of water that has been evaporated by deliberate activity of the house bees. A house bee who has just received nectar from a forager will place herself where there is a good flow of air in the hive. There, by head and tongue movements, she will regurgitate a small droplet onto the end of her proboscis, expose this to the airstream for a few seconds, then swallow it and produce another one. This is repeated eighty or ninety times in about twenty minutes, and in that time enough water has been evaporated to raise the sugar content by 15 percent. The house bee then seeks a cell in the storage area and deposits the nectar within. At this stage cells are not filled beyond two-thirds of their capacity. Evaporation continues from the exposed surface of the liquid in the cell, but during the night, when no fresh nectar is coming in from the fields, the house bees go again to these cells, take out some of the contents, and repeat the earlier process. All this time the fanners are circulating dry air through the hive and driving out the moisture. The roar of their wings can be heard many yards away. As the honey approaches its final density it is moved to fill the cells, and finally each cell is capped over with a layer of wax. The cappings prevent the re-entry of moisture from the atmosphere and keep the honey in perfect condition for a long time—years, in fact.

Because bees are able to gather large quantities of nectar in the summer and store it as honey for the winter, and because we ourselves find honey an attractive food, we are apt to forget that pollen is really the vital bee food. It alone contains

The house bees, who receive the nectar from the forager, are the processers and storers of honey.

Cells with sealed and unsealed honey. The cappings preserve the honey from the atmosphere.

the protein material and vitamins necessary for body building and growth. No larvae can be raised without pollen. Though honey contains mineral salts and other valuable materials in small quantities, it consists mainly of sugars, and as such is an energy food. Growing larvae require some, of course; but adults beyond the nursing stage actually need little else. Hence honey is the principal winter food for them.

Analysis of pollens from different plants show quite a wide variation in chemical content and food value to the bees. Those plants that depend on insects for fertilization tend to produce pollen of high nutritive value, whereas wind-pollinated plants usually produce poor quality pollen. Bees will gather from the poorer sources when little else is available. All pollens contain protein and are a source of vitamins of the B complex. Riboflavin and pantothenic acid are present in large quantities, and these undoubtedly play an important part both in the growth of larvae and in the nutrition of a laying queen.

Pollen is gathered both deliberately and accidentally. A bee who delves down into the flowers foraging for nectar must inevitably trap pollen grains in its body hairs, and so carries them home. But the quantity brought in this way is very small compared with that gathered deliberately. A pollen-gatherer at work ignores the plant nectaries and concentrates on the anthers for its booty, packing it onto its hind legs for the journey home. The so-called pollen baskets consist of a clump of long, spiny hairs on the tibia of each hind leg; the pollen is impaled on these as it is packed. First the bee takes the pollen from the flower with its front feet, moistens it with the tongue, and then passes it back from one leg to another on the opposite side. The right leg packs the left basket and vice versa. During the gathering the bee occasionally takes time out to transfer the pollen to the pollen baskets, but the final packing and body cleaning takes place during the flight home. The highly skillful operations are performed at extraordinary speed. The loads of pollen, though very bulky, weigh 12 to 25 milligrams, less than a load of nectar. When the pollen collector get home it seeks a cell in a pollen storage area and kicks off its burden into it. The subsequent treatment of the pollen, however, and its final packing in the comb are again the work of the house bees.

In flight the laden pollen-bearer carries its hind legs in a lowered position, and as it lands at the front of the hive we can easily see the two brightly colored masses it has brought home. Each lump will be uniform, for the overwhelming majority of honey bees on foraging flights are constant to one species of flower. This is one of their assets in the pollination of farm crops. But different members of one colony will be working on several species at the same time, and if we know the characteristic colors of various pollens, we are able to recognize them—bright orange for the dandelion, yellow-green for apple, pale brown for white clover, light blue for fireweed, and almost black for the poppy. It is a fascinating study for those who love bees or flowers.

Bees need pollen for protein, but flowers depend on this male substance to form seeds. Bees fertilize the plants by brushing pollen off their bodies as they go from flower to flower.

The viability of pollen as male plant cells is soon lost after leaving the flower, but that in itself does not affect the bee, who uses it as a source of protein food. The bigger problem for her is that the pollen is readily decomposed by molds and other micro-organisms. How then does she manage to preserve it all through winter until spring? Fortunately, ripe honey, with its high sugar content, is an excellent preservative. Some is mixed with the pollen as it is packed into the storage combs, the house bees ramming it down tightly with their heads. When a cell is about two-thirds full the remaining space is filled with honey. Sealed over with wax, the contents then remain usable for a long time.

6. senses and patterns of behavior

Move a hive from its original position, even as little as three feet, and you will soon see bees flying around the old spot in great confusion. So precisely have they located the hive entrance that even a minor change will bewilder them, and it will take them some time to reorient themselves. The older foragers will continue for several days to come to where the entrance used to be, hesitate briefly, then turn toward the new place. Their homing memory is so accurate that even raising or lowering the hive entrance by a few inches will hinder free flight for a time. The bees do recognize landmarks and will be mildly confused if you remove the vegetation from around their hive. Move the hive more than a few yards, and the foragers may never find their way home again. However, if the hive is moved to a position beyond their normal flying range of about two miles and the bees then released, they will appreciate the unfamiliar surroundings and quickly learn the hive's new location. This homing instinct is a convenience to commercial honey producers, who frequently move their bees around the countryside.

Experiments have taught us a great deal about homing navigation. For instance, it is quite easy to train foragers from a particular colony to make regular visits to a dish of sugar syrup; and by painting spots of color on their backs, it is possible to recognize those who have made the trip a number of times. Suppose the dish has been in a position two hundred yards due south of the hive for some time. Then later, while a number of the marked bees are on the dish sucking up syrup, the dish is picked up and carried to a spot two hundred yards due north of the hive. Each bee as it takes off with a loaded honey sac will now fly north, as it has been accustomed to do. Having flown about two hundred yards in the wrong direction, the bee becomes confused and starts to fly around in larger and larger circles. Finally it makes a direct flight to the hive, having spent two to four minutes on the short journey from the dish. A memory pattern, which included direction and distance, has been built up for the trips to and from the feeding place; this was made useless by relocating the dish. The bewildered bee had to fly around until some landmark recalled another pattern into operation to get it home. Such an experiment creates unnatural conditions, of course. Ordinarily the memory pattern is of the utmost value to the bee.

What we know of the world we have learned through our five senses. Today we are able to learn more than our forefathers did because science has added optical and electronic extensions to two of the senses. An insect's world is different from ours, because the insect's senses do not work in the same way or over the same range as ours. Man's dominant sense is sight; theirs is probably smell. We cannot really interpret their lives, however objective we try to be.

The sense of sight is a good example. Bees have eyes, but their vision does not correspond to ours because of the entirely different structure. The bee's compound eye consists of a large number of tiny fixed eyes, called ommatidia, grouped tightly together, about 6,000 on each side of a worker's head, fewer on a queen. The 8,500 ommatidia of a drone's compound eye are larger than those of the worker and queen and occupy a greater area of the head. Each ommatidium is a long tapered prism, with a sensory base within the head. The wide outer ends form the lens facets that cover the curved surface over the top and front of the head. Each has a very narrow field of view, and owing to the surface curvature, no two receive the identical images. There is no focusing mechanism; a bee must see a sort of mosaic of the scene around it. Such vision is most useful at close range, within a few feet.

What the compound eye does extremely well is detect movement. An object passing a series of facets in turn produces a succession of visual stimuli to which the insect can react very quickly. Conversely, a bee in flight receives from the objects it passes a sort of flicker pattern that can be memorized for navigation purposes. That is what a landmark resolves itself into for the bee; it is not a stationary object, with a shape and size that can be appreciated simultaneously. This is, after all, similar to what we do on a larger scale and at slower speed when we memorize our way through a city by noting the various streets and buildings.

Practically all winged insects have, in addition to the compound eyes, a group of three simple eyes situated between the upper areas of the compound eyes at the top of the head. Their purpose is not really known; they do not seem to belong to the visual system at all. From their structure it seems unlikely that they can form any sort of image, but experiments have shown that they are very sensitive to changes in light intensity. Possibly through this capacity they transmit stimuli to the wing muscles and so exercise some control over flight.

Any account of the senses and behavior of honeybees must mention the brilliant experimental work and discoveries of the Austrian naturalist Karl von Frisch. He has devoted a long lifetime to the subject, mainly at the universities of Munich and Graz, and his results have received world acclaim. His great and original work on the bee dances and their use as a language opened up a new field of study in animal behavior. A good deal of what we know about bee vision is also due to him, especially with regard to the bee's sensitivity to color and response to polarized light.

Light is said to be polarized when all the waves are vibrating in one plane, which normally they are not. Our eyes are completely unable to detect polarization, although we can see results of it with artificial aids. The reflected light from a blue sky is very strongly polarized in a plane relative to the position of the sun. Von Frisch found that bees recognized this, and that in conjunction with their time sense used it as an aid to navigation. Even on a cloudy day enough polarized rays penetrate to provide the bees with an accurate compass. Apart from clouds, the sun might be obscured by trees, rocks, or mountains; but quite a small patch of blue sky will suffice. Perhaps this is ample compensation for the bee's lack of sharp vision.

If nature evolved coloration of flowers to attract insects and so effect pollination, it would be logical to think that pollinating insects have color vision. Von Frisch, with a series of experiments in which bees were trained to visit dishes of sugar syrup on colored cards, contributed most of our present knowledge. In the first experiments he set empty dishes on cards of various shades of gray and one dish of syrup on either a yellow or a blue card. After the bees were given a period of training, the positions of the cards with the dishes were interchanged, but the bees readily found the dish on the colored card. When the food dish was moved to one of the gray cards, the bees still went to the colored card first before finding the syrup by the sense of smell. The food dish was then replaced with an empty one, and the bees searched continually around the colored card, trying to find it. Thus the bees recognized the color and not merely the intensity of reflected light, as a color-blind creature might have done.

The next thing was to determine which colors bees could distinguish, and whether they had any preferences. Here again differences between human and insect vision raised a problem. As early as 1895 it was suggested that insects' eyes might respond to ultraviolet light, which, of course, ours do not. Subsequent work had proved this to be true, particularly with bees, so von Frisch had to be sure that he knew the ultraviolet content of the light reflected from any of his cards in order to arrive at correct conclusions. To human beings, white light is the combination of the seven colors seen in a rainbow, violet to red; we can distinguish about sixty shades of color within that range. Bees recognize only four colors, one of which is ultraviolet. White light to a bee is a combination of those four: ultraviolet, blue, blue-green, and yellow. The bee is unable to perceive red at all; it appears black to her. It seems that the white that comprises the four colors is not so striking to a bee as a single color or combinations of two or three colors. Two white cards may look the same to us, but if one card reflects a lot of the ultraviolet light from the sun and the other does not, they will not appear the same to a bee. The second one, probably seen as blue-green, would be more attractive. Many flowers reflect a good deal of ultraviolet; the red poppy is one. The bee does not see it as black and is attracted to it. All other things being equal, bees seem to prefer blue flowers, but selection is associated with the scent and other qualities of the food present. The overriding factor in attracting bees is the sugar content of the nectar; high concentration is always preferred.

Scent plays a very important part in the insect–flower relationship. Again von Frisch devised experiments to study this, putting dishes of syrup inside boxes with holes through which the bees could enter. Bees were trained to visit a box in which the food had been scented with orange or peppermint. Then several more boxes were arranged around the same spot, containing syrups of different scents. When the trained bees returned they were at first confused, but finally the majority entered the box containing the syrup with the original scent. Given a choice over a long period, the bees showed an order of preference for the various scents used, possibly related to the floral scents to which they were accustomed.

It is not surprising that bees should be able to distinguish different colors and scents, for these are two things that we, too, associate with flowers. Not every kind of flower produces worthwhile quantities of nectar and pollen; in some the nectar is accessible only to creatures with tongues longer than that of the honeybee. Scent and color help the bees to recognize the flowers most useful to them, and the ability to memorize is useful on future trips.

Scent plays a big part in a bee's recognition of its fellows. Watch two bees as they meet on the comb or on the outside of the hive; they immediately begin to stroke each other's heads with their antennae. This is one way for a guard bee to distinguish between friend and foe, of course, but the behavior is almost continuous and undoubtedly plays a part in communication between members of the colony. A great many functions, some not yet fully understood, are performed by antennae. They are rarely still, and it is mainly through them that the bee maintains consciousness of its surroundings. To call them 'feelers' is to oversimplify their function, although the sense of touch in the hairs at the ends is very acute. Remarkable in their versatility, these organs are sensitive to changes in air pressure and are used for smell, taste, water perception, and temperature perception as well. They may even include a form of hearing.

The first part of the antenna of a honeybee is a short, thick piece attached to the head by a ball-and-socket joint. It is free to move in any direction. The second longer and flexible part is made of a series of jointed sections. There are hairs of several types, and under the microscope, some highly distinctive cell structures are visible on the surface. Scent perception is very acute here. In the search for food, in the recognition of fellow bees, in maintaining contact with the queen, the sense of smell is most important to a bee—so important that there are subsidiary odor receptors on other parts of the body. Whether water actually has a smell to bees we don't know, but at least their antennae are sensitive to the presence of water vapor and can lead them to the source of water. The sensitivity of the antennae to air pressure has a number of uses. As two adjacent objects come closer together there will be a slight rise in air pressure between them. The antennae's sensitivity to this probably enables the bees to move around without colliding in the darkness of the hive. Air pressure on the antennae in flight acts as a speed indicator, and actual movements of the antennae during flight plays a

The bees' antennae are sensitive to water vapor and can guide them easily to the source.

part in orientation and distance perception. The bee memorizes the manner and durations of the deflections, which act as a guide. Gravity may also be sensed by the antennae, but it has recently been discovered that organs for this purpose exist in the neck and the narrow petiole that connects the abdomen to the thorax.

Whether or not bees can hear is an old controversy. Some able experimenters in the past concluded that bees do not hear, but they probably erred by testing only with sounds that were significant to the human ear. Others, because of the many distinctive sounds that are heard in the hive and the vibratory motions that bees so often make, think that these must be interpreted in some way that at least corresponds to hearing. Recent experiments show that the bees' language is probably phonetic as well as kinetic. Mammals and birds receive sounds that are transmitted through air and in general are sensitive to a wide range of frequencies—

that is, many different sounds. Other creatures may not be able to detect sound waves in air at all, but are nevertheless sensitive to vibrations traveling through other media. Fish, for instance, respond quickly to vibrations in water. But the response might be a very narrow one that includes only those sounds or vibrations that are of biological importance to the particular animal. The grasshopper receives the strident call of its mate, but is probably unable to hear anything else.

Getting bees to respond to any sounds transmitted through air has met with little success. Recently, however, positive results have been obtained in causing natural hive sounds to travel through such solid material as the wooden structure of an observation hive. Tape recordings of specific sounds have been made—for instance, a young queen piping—and the loudspeaker laid on the hive during playback. Though the volume was kept quite low, the bees reacted exactly as they would have in the presence of a young queen, even to leaving the hive as a swarm. The vibrations traveled through the wood and along the combs. Quite possibly their aural sense is in their feet. Why not? We know that they can taste and smell that way. However, it is still possible that the antennae, too, have some part in sound perception.

Somewhere a bee has a built-in clock, or so it seems, for it has a very good sense of time. Bees can be trained to visit artificial food supplies at definite times each day. This sense is valuable to them in the exploitation of natural food sources, for it is well known that the flowers of many plants yield their nectar or pollen during certain periods of the day. Pear blossoms, for instance, seem to be worked in the morning up to about 10 o'clock then the bees switch to other sources that yield later in the day. Consider the bee that makes a long trip to a certain group of flowers, say, a mile or more; it memorizes a navigation pattern, using the polarized light from the sky. Two hours after its return the bee starts out to repeat the trip. The sun has moved around, and the plane of polarization with it, but the bee makes no mistake in direction. Its time sense, coupled with an instinctive knowledge of the sun's movement through the day, has automatically made allowance for this.

Some of the most interesting experimental work on the time sense was done with bees whose hives were kept in completely dark rooms, at constant temperature and humidity, so that they could not tell day from night. (Although the rooms were dark to the bees, a red light could be used for the benefit of the investigators.) The bees were trained to feed from dishes of sugar syrup, placed a few feet from the hives so they could run to and from them along the tables. When the dishes were put out at the same time each day and left for two hours the bees, after a few days, would run out quite readily from the hives during this period, whereas few bees came out at other times. They continued to come out on subsequent days at the same time, even when the dishes were no longer there. It was easy to train bees to feed at intervals of six, eight, or twelve hours, but their timing became less accurate when the intervals were seventeen or nineteen hours. It appears that their sense of time works in a twenty-four-hour rhythm and is independent of the bees' perception of night and day. Some bees in these experiments had been raised and maintained entirely in darkness, never seeing light or the outside world, but they reacted just the same as the others.

It is important in the bee world that in a constantly changing population of many thousands an individual bee must be able to recognize its community members, otherwise bees from another colony might enter the nest and steal the food. This can happen—but not without a fight, unless the robbed colony is very weak and disorganized. Observations of colony behavior by many beekeepers have led to the conclusion that recognition is by smell, and scientific experiments have proved the opinion to be correct. There is an odor common to the bees of one colony and readily recognizable among the members. It is conceivable that two distinct colonies, each having a different hereditary background, would also have a different natural odor; but this would not apply in every case. A swarm leaves its parent colony and sets up a home near by. In a matter of days the two groups will be antagonistic toward each other if brought together. A beekeeper may take two lots of workers from one hive and introduce sister queens, one to each lot, but again there may be hostility if he tries to mix some of these bees a week or so later. If sister groups of bees can acquire different odors being separated for a short time, some explanation other than heredity must be sought.

The answer is found in the study of a fundamental habit of social insects: recriprocal food exchange. It is common to see two bees sharing food in the hive,

Reciprocal food exchange makes it possible for the members of the hive to recognize each other. Sharing the same diet, they also exude the same colony smell.

The guard bees pick up the odor of the stranger, whether he be a robber bee or an innocent intruder. The guard inspects the newcomer, then attacks her. Very shortly reinforcements arrive; the enemy is overcome and ejected from the hive.

62

tongues together, each moving its antennae rapidly on the other's head. Food, just brought in or taken from the storage cells, is continually being passed from bee to bee. So every bee in the colony has exactly the same diet, which is unlikely to have precisely the same chemical composition as the diet in another hive, however close by. The excretion products will differ too, marking the body odor. If, as is probable, gland products are exchanged as well, then these will also have slight variations, according to the food being consumed. There is a definite colony odor, which can change with the consumption of honey and pollen from different flowers, but which is at any one time peculiar to a single colony.

Bees sometimes enter the wrong hive accidentally; a strong wind may blow them off course, or they may mistake the entrance of an alien hive for theirs. They will almost always be challenged by the guard bees, who pick up the strange scent with their antennae. A laden forager is usually accepted and allowed in; any other alien bee is in trouble. It will be seized by several of the guards, who will propel it away from the entrance. In times of food shortage, when robbing between colonies is liable to take place, the intruder will be killed and its body thrown out. Large-scale robbing attacks do take place occasionally; generally a strong colony attacks a weak one. In the fall when the main nectar-bearing plants have gone, old foragers will go around looking for anything sweet anywhere. A number of them may attempt to enter a strange hive, and then a fight ensues; but if only one should get in and come out with stolen honey, the first barrier is down. That robber goes home, passes on the necessary information to her sisters, and the attack is on. Both sides suffer many casualties. A strong colony will hold its own and finally defeat the raider; a weak one will give up after a time. Sometimes a colony becomes so demoralized that its members join forces with the raiders, taking their own treasures to the enemy's castle. Its queen will be destroyed and the combs torn down. Nature favors the strong; perhaps the weak colony would have had little chance of surviving the winter.

When a swarm enters a new home the first arrivals at the entrance assume an odd position, with the tips of their abdomens high in the air, and fan their wings vigorously; others join them as the throng moves in. Near the end of the abdomen is an opening exposing a small white area. This is the scent-producing Nassanoff gland, named after the biologist who first described its function. The scent is dispersed into the air to summon the other bees to the new home; and the faint musty smell can be detected by the human nose when a number of bees are so engaged. This is less a specific colony smell than a honeybee smell belonging to the species. It is effective for several yards. Normally any bee will respond to it, but undoubtedly there is a slight colony differentiation that serves a purpose at times. The Nassanoff gland is in frequent use. A homecoming forager may stand at the hive entrance sending out the message so that others returning may find their way in quickly. A violently disturbed colony will soon have its fanners directing members back to the home and comb. In these circumstances, and with a homing

The Nassanoff gland emits a special honeybee smell. A homecoming forager may stand at the hive entrance, fanning vigorously to help orient members of the colony.

swarm, a few bees from neighboring colonies may answer the call, but no fighting takes place.

Some years ago I saw a striking example of the use of the scent gland in the reorientation of a colony that had suffered a disaster. It had a natural nest in a hollow tree, about eighteen feet above the ground. One night the tree was blown down in a storm. On the following morning I was asked to go to the site and deal with the bees, as the owners wished to cut up and remove the fallen tree. I arrived there at about 11 A.M. As expected, a lot of bees were flying about; the entrance to their nest was now displaced several feet both vertically and horizontally from its original position. Nevertheless, there was a ring of fanners using their Nassanoff glands around the hole in the fallen trunk where the hive entrance was. And several bees, with loads of pollen on their legs, entered the hive, showing that they had been able to find it after a field trip.

I then had to add to their troubles by cutting open the tree, taking out the combs, and tying them into wood frames for transfer into a box. This done, the box was placed on the split part of the tree and left until dusk. By that time all the bees were settled in their new home, so they were shut up and taken away to my apiary. The colony not only survived this treatment, but eventually prospered.

7. the language and mind of the bees

The story of the language of the bees has been growing steadily for the past forty years, and during this time Professor von Frisch has periodically published the results of his original research. His own colleagues, along with scientific investigators of many other countries, have confirmed and elaborated the work, so that what once seemed incredible has now received acceptance everywhere: There exists in the honeybee a level of communication higher than that in any other animal apart from man, and this above all else accounts for its efficiency in the gathering of food. The acute senses, the wonderful navigational ability, are coordinated through the interpretation of a language; and we must marvel, with von Frisch, that it all takes place in a brain 'no larger than a grain of millet.'

The existence of some form of communication is easily demonstrated. If a small amount of honey is put into an open dish and placed about twenty yards from some hives, it may take a while, maybe several hours, before a bee flying nearby picks up the scent and alights to feed. Yet within a few minutes after the bee has returned home, several more will arrive at the dish. In half an hour there might be a hundred or more, and by marking them one can clearly show they all belong to the same hive. Another experiment is even more convincing. Instead of waiting for the honey to be found by chance, a bee is gently picked up from the hive entrance, marked, and taken to the dish. Its discomfort forgotten the moment it comes into contact with the honey, the bee will fill itself with the treasure and return home. Soon there will be others feeding, but the first bee is not with this group. It may be another quarter of an hour before she returns. The other bees have not been led to the food source; they have been directed. These simple experiments, which can be repeated by anyone, were von Frisch's basic procedure in the training and observation of foraging bees. Coupled with this was his long study of the behavior of the bees at home, as seen in a glass-sided hive.

What has been suggested so far is that the majority of foragers do not go searching for food at random, and that once a good source has been discovered, large numbers are quickly recruited to exploit it. This is true. A small number of the total force act as scouts, or searchers. They explore the territory around the hive at gradually increasing distances and probably rely on scent to find the flowers in the first place. When a searcher returns home it communicates to others in the hive the most precise information about its findings—the food's odor and taste, and its direction and distance from the hive.

That some bees appeared to dance on the combs with quick shivering motions whenever pollen and nectar were being brought into the hive had frequently been observed. As long ago as 1788 Father Spitzner had suggested that these bees were giving information about the food sources to others. Nobody followed up this suggestion for over a hundred years; then von Frisch began to unfold the story of the dancing bees.

The dance is performed by any forager that has just returned from the fields with a load of nectar or pollen. In its simplest form it describes a source close to the hive, within one hundred yards. Von Frisch calls this the 'round dance.' The bee runs in small circles in one spot on the comb, alternately to the left and right. After a minute or so she may move to another spot and repeat the performance there. While she is dancing a small group of bees will gather around her excitedly and keep touching her body with their antennae. Occasionally the dancer stops, and if she is a nectar-gatherer, she regurgitates a little of the nectar onto the end of her tongue. The others take it, and knowing now both the aroma and the taste of the food, fly out to find it. Circling, they are soon able to pick up the scent and find the flowers they are looking for. Once the source is located, future flights will go directly to it. The richer the source, the more vigorously the dancer performs, and the greater the number of recruits obtained. If the food is abundant and many bees go out to collect it, the first to reach the flowers will open their scent glands and fan for a few moments, thus calling the others to the source.

The round dance is comparatively simple. With more distant sources the dances convey much more precise and detailed information. The other foragers are even given the direction in which to fly and the distance. If the source is more than one hundred yards away, the round dance changes to the 'wagtail dance.' The pattern of this is sometimes described as a figure eight, perhaps better visualized as two half circles made in opposite directions, with a straight run in between, forming a common diameter. It is this straight run that is important, and during it the dancer wags her abdomen vigorously. Should the dance take place on a horizontal surface such as a landing place at the hive entrance, the run is made in a line directly toward the feeding place. But it is rarely as simple as that; more often the dancer is on the vertical face of a comb. Then the run bears a relationship to the position of the sun in the sky at the time, and gravity is a factor. A run vertically upward indicates the food source is directly toward the sun; a downward run indicates it is away from the sun. All other directions are shown by the amount of deviation from the vertical, up or down. For instance, if the wagging bee runs upward at an angle of 30 degrees to the left of the vertical, then the source is in a direction 30 degrees to the left of the sun. Every possible direction can be given and interpreted with amazing accuracy.

The level of communication in the honeybee is second only to that of man. The dances of the bees are really a language by which they tell their sisters how to reach the sources of nectar.

Distance is communicated by the rate at which the dance is performed. The dancer probably indicates the amount of energy required to make the flight, rather than the distance as such, but it comes to the same thing. Using his marked bees that were trained to visit food sources at various distances, von Frisch found that the farther the distance, the slower the dance. He also found that there was some variation, according to whether the bee had to fly into a head wind or

The sounds associated with the wagtail dance play a significant role in communication. When the dance is silent, the bees do not seek the nectar source.

before a tail wind. This, of course, would influence the time and energy needed for the journey. If the food was two hundred yards from the hive, there would be about seven complete dance cycles every fifteen seconds. At the other extreme, four miles away, only two cycles were completed in that time. The slower movements created less general excitement; therefore fewer bees tended to be recruited to fly to the distant source. However, those that did contact the dancer were excited, stroked with their antennae in the usual way, and accepted proffered samples of food. The greatest stimulation is always to the nearest and richest sources of food, yet bees will fly up to five miles when no nectar and pollen are available near by.

The accuracy with which recruits found the food sources at the longest distances was within 150 yards; scent would guide them the rest of the way. The nearer the source, the greater the accuracy. When a large area of ground is covered with the same flowering plant, individual foragers continue to return to the same few square feet day after day. Having located a profitable spot, they work at it and do not waste time flying here and there. During the first trip to a new source, using information dispensed in the hive, a bee will begin to memorize landmarks and, finally, the color of the flowers sought. Succeeding visits can then be made more easily, and other flowers of the same kind in the immediate neighborhood are quickly found. When bees are working a known source the direction of the dances on the combs can be seen to change gradually during the day as the sun follows its course. The bee that has already learned the location makes its own navigational adjustments through its time sense.

The dance patterns outlined above are not the only ones used in the hive. The 'whirr dance' is used in swarming, and there is also a 'scrubbing dance,' which seems to be associated with hive cleaning and the use of propolis. The significance of this and other possible dances are not yet understood. The wagtail dance does seem to be the most important, and it has at least one other purpose in addition to food source communication: to direct bees in a swarm to their new home.

The partial failure in the supply of queen substance seems to initiate the swarming impulse, and that triggers off a sequence of events in the hive that upsets its normal rhythm. One sign is the reluctance on the part of the house bees to relieve foragers of their loads of nectar in the two or three days before swarming. Foraging activity declines abuptly, and with it the interest in pollen and nectar dances. This in turn produces a change in the behavior of searcher bees. They no longer go looking for food; instead they scour the neighborhood seeking possible nesting places. Their findings are communicated to other foragers through wagtail dances.

Observant beekeepers have often anticipated a swarm by a day or two by noticing inquisitive bees flying around or in and out of odd boxes, roof eaves, and particularly unoccupied hives. The scent of these, if they have previously been tenanted, is very attractive, and it is not uncommon for the searchers to start moving debris from them. Using a 'bait hive' to catch stray swarms is a standard apiary practice. Once again the dancing in the hive encourages recruits, who will make further inspections of the sites. These dances, however, do not end after a few minutes, but may go on for hours. Several possible nesting places may be indicated at the same time, but the excitement engendered is at first not so great as with the food dances. The purpose seems to be mainly a conditioning of the colony for the next phase of swarming.

At what time the swarm leaves the hive is determined by the condition of the queen cells and the weather. One queen cell, at least, will have reached the sealing stage before the swarm goes out with the existing queen. When the time does arrive it is the searchers who initiate the move. They rapidly increase the vigor of their dances and move to different parts of the hive at frequent intervals. Excitement among the other bees builds up. Then, all within a few minutes, the wagtail dance changes to the whirr dance, in which the bees force their way through the hive with rapidly vibrating abdomens, their wings making a loud whirring sound; hundreds more soon join in, the whirr becomes a roar, and the bees come tumbling out of the hive. This activity of the dancing bees partly explains why a swarm settles first in a place not far from its hive. Now a 'debate' takes place to decide which of the several sites offered by the searchers shall be selected.

As soon as the cluster is settled on the bush or tree bough, the dancers begin to perform again on the outside of it. They will continue to do so as long as the swarm remains there, the direction of the wagtail runs changing with the movement of the sun across the sky. At intervals, individual bees break away to continue their exploration. Should the cluster stay overnight, the dances continue, the bee's time sense controlling a gradual change of direction, so that by morning all are oriented to the rising sun. The vigor of the dances, used in food searches to indicate richness of source, now indicates the desirability of a possible nesting site. Instinctively the searchers know what they need. Shelter from strong winds is a major requirement; food must be available nearby, and the nest easy to defend. As some trees yield nectar and many more are good sources of pollen in the spring, and as a hollow tree is a favorite nesting place, wooded country is naturally attractive to swarms. Dense forest, however, is not, for adjacent areas of low-growing plants are needed to provide the summer forage. Favorable reaction to a site is automatic, and the dancers, rather than recruit other bees, now communicate their enthusiasm to each other. One who is dancing apathetically because its site has failed to excite it will be influenced by a neighbor, whose dance is livelier, and will change its own pattern to that one. One by one the poorer choices are dropped, and in due course—sometimes within minutes, often after several hours—the selection is made. The swarm is ready for a purposeful flight to its new home. Now there is repetition of earlier behavior; the searchers become excited, start the whirr dance, and in moments the whole swarm is in the air. Led by the searcher bees, the swarm travels in a direct line to the chosen site. A prime swarm will travel only in the middle hours of the day, so if the decision has been reached after about 4 P.M., the move will be postponed until the next day. The foraging bees that leave with a swarm seem to cancel the memory of their old site completely, and quickly learn to locate the new one; but if during the move the queen should be lost, they will lead the entire swarm back to the old home to await the birth of a new queen.

Our interpretations of the bee dances are necessarily made through the glass sides of an observation hive. Obviously none of the bees can see the pattern of movement as we can. In any case, as the food dances normally take place in complete darkness, the bees' reaction is not a visual one at all; other senses must be involved. With the aid of a tape recorder it has been found that the dancers emit sound impulses that correspond to the rhythm of the visual movements. Tests have shown that other bees also respond to these recordings. Sound vibrations are certainly a communicating factor. Harald Esch, who worked with Von Frisch in 1960, conducted a series of experiments that showed the sounds associated with the wagtail dance played a significant role in communication. Often foragers returning to the hive would perform silent dances. Esch observed over 15,000 of these; all of them failed to guide bees to the nectar source.

If, as some think, the acquirement of speech induced the great development of human intelligence, then the dance language of the bees, together with their seemingly high abilities in other areas, seems to suggest that these insects have, in their own line of evolution, reached a state comparable to the highest of mammals. If they are not intelligent, then some explanation is required. There is no simple all-embracing definition of intelligence. The term is usually defined within context and is often used loosely. To pursue the subject is beyond the scope of this book, but in considering the behavior of the honeybee, we should remember that a large part of human behavior also derives from simple reflexes, instincts, and acquired social patterns.

Intelligence involves memory, coordination of the senses, and a capacity to learn by experience. All animals have these things in some degree. Certainly the bee's senses are well coordinated, and the work of the forager alone gives evidence of memory and the ability to learn within limitations. But more than this is implied. A human being is able to select at will from information that the senses provide, draw at will from a memory that extends over most of a lifetime, and use this knowledge not only to premeditate his own actions but also to anticipate events. There is no evidence that a bee can do these things. Whatever it does is either purely instinctive or a direct reaction to external stimuli, although the initial stimulus does often start off a complex chain of action that is itself instinctive. Memory is short and maintained only by repetition of some behavior pattern. Above all, the human maintains a continuous consciousness of itself; nothing in insect behavior suggests that this quality exists in them.

Instincts are a kind of racial memory. Bees do not have to acquire the skill to build comb; the skill is there, and wonderful in that the memory involves cooperation between numbers of individuals. But we have seen how the bee colony is really a single organism. Birds do not have to learn how to build their nests or where to travel on migratory flight. Through millions of experiments over countless generations, those patterns that developed along lines beneficial to the species survived; the others did not. The offspring inherited the minute differences in nerve and brain structure, and it tended to make them behave in the same way. So by natural selection a pattern of living was developed that was suitable for the species. The instincts of insects are very highly developed but less flexible than those of birds and mammals, for their great period of development occurred earlier in history. Perhaps they are incapable of making further major changes.

All social animals are sensitive to what are called 'intention movements' on the part of their fellows. One individual makes a slight movement in preparation for some action, and the rest know immediately what it is going to do. Mutual safety depends on this sense. A flock of starlings feeding on the ground will rise into the air almost simultaneously. One bird has sensed danger. In a fraction of a second it has made slight movements of the body in preparation for flight. Neighboring birds are alerted; and by the time the first one is off the ground, the stimulus has traveled like a high-speed wave through the flock, and all rise into the air. Two people are sitting in a room. One will know that the other intends to leave the room before the latter has left the chair, and without a word being spoken. A glance toward the door and a slight movement of the body have betrayed the intention.

Simple intention movements play a large part in the behavior of a bee colony. The spread of alarm by the guard bees is a good example. But the superorganism is conscious of its needs and intentions as a whole. The frequent sensual contact between individuals through the antennae and the constant process of food sharing maintain a common purpose. Instinctive patterns are brought into operation according to the conditions and needs of the moment. The lack of queen substance induces the waxmakers and nurse bees to begin building cells. A shortage of water, pollen, or nectar among the nurse bees is communicated to the foragers by actions that 'ask' them to go out and seek these things. When a forager has received such a stimulus from a nurse bee it will automatically be attracted to a dancer, who will give it the necessary information for its mission.

In this way the colony can be considered to have a mass mind that controls its behavior and destiny as a whole. That this mind is a purely mechanical and instinctive one does not detract from its intricacy. The hive mind does, after all, operate through the nervous system of the individual bee, the worker in particular; so once again we come back to this marvelous little creature.

8. the rhythm
of the seasons

Spring

All life follows a rhythmic pattern attuned to the seasons of the year. Spring in the temperate zones is the time of a great awakening. To the honeybee, whose existence depends on making full use of the wealth from summer flowers, spring brings a tremendous urge for activity. The stirrings begin before any flowers are seen and while the snow is still on the ground. But the hours of daylight are getting longer, and the midday sun a little warmer. The great summer population of the hive cannot come overnight; a start must be made now.

During the quiet clustering period of winter the number of bees in the hive has been decreasing; the field bees of the fall have long since gone. Foragers of the new season have conditions of wind and low temperatures to contend with that the summer bees never know. Many will not return from trips to fetch water or to gather pollen from the earliest spring flowers. Now the young bees who have lived through the winter, with developed but unused brood-food glands, will begin to take up their suspended nursing duties.

The temperature in the center of the cluster will be at the normal brood-rearing level of 90–95 degrees; and it is here that the queen will start to lay eggs, in her usual methodical fashion but in small numbers, so that there will be patches of brood on adjacent combs. In three weeks the new workers begin to emerge, and the cells are cleaned out for the queen to lay in them again. The brood area cannot be extended much yet, for weather conditions are still severe outside. It is likely, too, that the colony has not actually grown in size, for the number of new young bees may be less than the number of old ones that have died in the meantime. Clearly this is a critical situation, one that may exist for some weeks. It is difficult to know when it will end, for both colony and locality conditions vary, but in those parts of the Northern Hemisphere that have fairly severe winters it may be toward the end of March. At some time in these brightening days the number of young bees appearing will exceed the mortality rate of the old. The crisis is past. From now on, expansion continues at an ever-increasing pace. At this time the population may be around ten thousand; two months later it may swell to fifty thousand.

Until now nearly all the food required to raise brood has had to come from either winter stores or the bodily reserves of the nurse bees. True, the foragers have eagerly sought the early flowers, but valuable though their work has been, the total quantity of food gathered has been small. The same amount of food needed to keep the quiescent winter cluster going for a week or more is now needed each day in the raising of brood; the consumption rises from a few ounces a week to several pounds.

The colony that went into winter with a large stock of food reaps full benefit and forges ahead; the less fortunate develop more slowly. It is amazing, though, how some colonies can survive in the spring with only enough food for a day-to-day existence, but these lag a long way behind in growth. The winter workers didn't cover all the combs in the hive; there were fewer bees than in the summer, and as their numbers dwindled and the food was consumed more combs became vacant. Unoccupied comb deteriorates in the winter atmosphere and suffers from wax moth larvae and other small invaders, sometimes even large ones like mice. Lying below the combs are the old cappings, dead bees, and other debris.

Spring is the time for cleaning. As soon as there is a really warm spell the house bees get busy; they grasp bits of stuff in their mandibles and carry them outside. The larger pieces and dead bees are dragged and pushed out of the hive. There is quite a heap by the end of the day. As the colony expands and more cells are needed for brood more cleaning will be done. Bits of dried up and moldy pollen will be thrown out, damaged combs repaired, and extensions added to them where necessary.

Once the really cold weather has gone and the flush of spring flowers comes, growth proceeds at a tremendous pace. The brood limit will be set either by the number of nurses available or by the area in which the bees can maintain the necessary temperature. The limit keeps extending, provided the nest cavity is large enough, until the ultimate one is reached—the maximum egg-laying capacity of the queen.

Although the end of summer is the time when the robbing instinct is strongest in bees, it can arise in spring. A colony that is numerically weak but still has a fair store of food is a temptation to its neighbors, particularly if the entrance to its hive is too large to defend easily. Sometimes a colony may perish from natural causes, such as disease or the death of a queen, leaving food in the hive. Such a hive will almost certainly be cleaned out in the spring if there is another colony nearby.

Through the hard months, when every ounce of food is vital, there were no drones. Now, with rising prosperity and instincts dictating a future need for them, the males begin to appear. With drones on the wing, thousands of workers already in the hive, thousands more in embryo in the comb cells, and still more to come as the queen goes on laying, the life of the colony is rising to its peak. It is ready to take full advantage of the bounty of nectar that the summer flowers will offer.

Summer

Summer is the time of the colony's fulfillment. At the peak of its growth, it is ready for reproduction and the renewal of its growing point. It is the time of harvest and preparation for yet another season.

The bee colony does not die of old age; it has within itself the power of replacement of its organs, including old or ineffective queens. Nevertheless, some colonies are lost through various hazards such as starvation, enemy attack, and disease. To survive and increase itself, the species must reproduce. So swarming takes place in late spring and early summer, while there is yet time to build and stock new nests and rear populations of young bees for the winter. Not every colony swarms every year, and the factors contributing to it are not all known. Weather certainly has a considerable influence. There are notable swarming years, and others when very little takes place. Always, however, a swarming colony is a strong and prosperous one, with workers of all ages, drones on the wing, a lot of sealed brood, and recently gathered nectar and pollen. Once the urge is upon the colony, changes take place that completely alter the hive routine and finally divide the family.

The queen is rising to the height of her laying powers. Her attendants, who may number twenty or more, have been almost force feeding her to maintain the huge output of eggs. One of the first visible signs of swarming preparations is the increasing aggressiveness of this attention. The mother is driven to the queen cups, which she normally ignores, and over a period of two or three days lays eggs in a number of them. Once the eggs have hatched and the queen larvae have begun to develop, the nurse bees show a complete reversal of attitude to their queen. Now they no longer seek to attend her at all; indeed, they often refuse her food when she solicits it from them. She begins to wander aimlessly about the combs as her egg laying rapidly diminishes. By the time the swarm is ready to leave the hive, and the queen with it, the queen's abdomen has shrunk to almost the size it was before she was mated. This is a wonderful provision of nature, for a swarm may have to fly some distance to a new home, an impossible feat for a queen with her ovaries full of eggs.

Weather permitting, the swarm will leave when the first of the queen cells is sealed, and it will be only a matter of days before there is a young virgin in the hive to replace the old mother. On a fine day, between 10 A.M. and 4 P.M., the time will come when the climax of all the preparation is reached. A number of bees may be noticed running in a restless manner up the face of the hive and around the entrance. The restlessness within soon raises the steady hum to the crescendo of the whirr dance, and like a living cascade the swarm pours from the hive. Straight up on the wing they whirl around, thousands upon thousands, until the air is thick with them for many yards around. The queen is never the first one out, and she may be near the last. Once again she appears to be literally driven off the combs and out of the hive. She will not be neglected from now on,

The bee colony is a superorganism that has the power to reproduce itself. Swarming is the simple division of the hive at a time of prosperity.

for a swarm is extremely conscious of the scent of its queen; without her it cannot fulfill its destiny. No positive move away from the immediate vicinity of the hive is made until she is in the throng. Because the queen is unaccustomed to flying, it may well be that she soon has to land on a nearby bush or tree branch. This encourages the swarm to settle and cluster there. It is rare for a prime swarm to travel more than a few hundred yards at first.

Clustering is a fundamental habit of honeybees, originating probably as a method of heat conservation, and still so used, especially in the winter. It also serves important social purposes in the colony organism, providing the closest possible contact between individuals, facilitating communication, and so maintaining unity. If a hundred or more bees are shaken from their combs into an empty box, which is then closed up and left, they will run about in a distressed state for a time; but within two hours they will form themselves into a cluster, hanging from an upper surface of the box, and remain that way until disturbed. The bees link together by hanging on to one another's legs, to form an interlacing network that distributes the mechanical stresses. With a swarm hanging on a tree branch, those members actually in contact with the branch must be supporting the weight of the pendant mass below them, but there is a frequent exchange of places between individuals, which prevents fatigue. As with a winter cluster in a

A swarm is extremely conscious of the scent of its queen. This queen was captured and placed under a sieve. Minutes later many of the workers found their mother and flocked to her.

Clustering is an instinctive social need that serves the bees well at swarming time. Clinging to one another's legs, the colony can reunite and communicate, as well as conserve heat, if they must remain in the open for any length of time.

Bees gorging from honey cells in preparation for swarming.

hive, there is a tight formation on the outer surface, with looser chains of bees within. The whole looks like a large oval football, and contains anywhere from fifteen thousand to thirty thousand bees, weighing from three to six pounds. During swarming, a brief but important phase of the honeybees' existence, the clustering habit serves it well.

About half the total population goes out with a swarm. Exactly how the choice is made is not known, but it consists mainly of young bees, the ones who have had the closest contact with the queen and who have played a major part in the preparations. Nature dictates the answer to the needs of the new hive. Comb builders and nurse bees are essential. Nevertheless, there are some bees of all ages, including a few drones, who probably get caught up in the excitement. Many foragers may be out in the fields when the swarm leaves, and of course the swarm will have a higher proportion of foragers as its bees age.

The departing bees have gorged themselves on honey from the comb cells, for fuel is needed for the journey, and wax glands must be ready for building comb. Should the weather deteriorate, the swarm may not be able to reach its final home for a day or two and will have to remain clustered in the open. The food they carry will last them about three days, so there is still a good chance of survival and eventual success. When the swarm has arrived at the new home the foraging members will fetch more food. In fact, they will begin work from the cluster in the open if the swarm remains there several hours or more. Occasionally a swarm makes an intermediate move to another clustering place, especially if the first spot was in full sun. Whether the final move comes after minutes or hours or days, it is dictated by the activity of the searcher bees. When the time comes and the whirr dance starts there is even less hesitation than when the bees originally left the hive. They are in the air in a few moments and away quickly in their serious game of follow-the-leader.

The first arrivals at the site land close to the cavity entrance and, with their scent glands open and wings fanning, call the rest in. The mass tends to gather below the hole and stream upward into it. As soon as the queen enters, the merry hum gets noticeably louder, and all quickly follow her inside. Within minutes, rubbish is thrown out and the waxmaking clusters begin to form. A newly established swarm works with astounding vigor; large areas of comb are built in a few days and the storing of nectar and pollen begun. There is, of course, no brood to feed until the queen has come back into lay. This may not be for several days, but time is valuable. It will be nearly a month before any new bees emerge from their cells, and in the meantime the aging population is dying off. Combs must be built and food stored in these early days.

Back in the parent hive the bees await the coming of a new queen so it can re-establish itself as a complete organism. The reduced population recovers somewhat as young workers emerge from the brood left by the old queen. If the swarm left early, the first virgin queen will emerge from her cell in six more days. Her first instinct will be to destroy her sisters in the other queen cells, but the bees may not allow her to do so. If there is a large hive population the reproductive urge may still be present, and other swarms will leave, taking virgin queens along. These are known as afterswarms, or casts. Two or three casts, each smaller than the one before, may leave on successive days, or if weather has delayed them, one large cast will leave, with several virgin queens. In this case, the death battle between the young queens takes place upon arrival at the new nesting place. A cast is much less predictable than a prime swarm, probably because young unmated queens are very active. It will come out of the hive at almost any time of the day, and often fly a long distance immediately. It is notable that virgins going out with a cast soon mate and come into lay very quickly in the new nest. Different strains of bees vary in their tendency to throw casts, some breaking themselves up into hopelessly small units at times. There is always one virgin left in the old hive. Sometimes this last one comes out with a small cast, and then returns. This seems to be a mating swarm, for a laying queen is usually found a few days later. In colonies that do not throw any casts, the first queen to

The honey flows attract others besides honeybees. The hover fly, at left, bears a remarkable resemblance to the honeybee with whom it is sharing an ivy flower.

appear after the swarm has left is permitted to destroy the others in their cells; she mates, and all is normal again. The continuity of the colony is assured, its vital organ renewed.

Biologically it seems odd that the old queen should go out with the prime swarm. In the natural order of things it is the young who go forth from home to seek new territories. Most likely this is a development of an ancestral migratory habit. Tropical species of honeybees in India and Malaya, closely related to *Apis mellifera*, habitually migrate from the dry plains to the hills in the hot season, returning again after the rains, when flowers are once more abundant. These bees reproduce by raising young queens during the spring nectar flows; and when the queens fly out to mate they leave with swarms. It is reasonable to think that our bees as they spread to the temperate climates modified the migratory act to one of reproductive swarming, as we know it. This view would regard casts as being parallel to the mating swarms of the other species.

The accumulation of honey in the hive for the winter larder is not a gradual process; it occurs in well-defined periods in which there are tremendous bursts of activity. There are specific occasions when nectar is available in large quantities, known to beekeepers as 'honey flows,' although 'nectar flows' is more strictly accurate. The bees take full advantage of these, and large amounts are brought into the hives. A subtle combination of soil conditions, air temperature, and humidity causes the plant nectaries to produce an abundance, where previously it has been negligible. The bees react quickly and gather it with terrific energy from morning till night. Perhaps a field of clover has been in bloom for a couple of weeks. Here and there bees have visited the flowers, and some loads of clover pollen have gone into the hive; but there has been no great rush and no excitement, and the hive weight has changed very little. Then overnight all is changed, the bees come tumbling out of the hive in a hurry and often on the wing before they are out of the hive entrance. Equally large numbers, abdomens distended, land heavily in front of the hive before running in. In the air we can see the 'bee line'—workers streaming to and fro along an aerial lane leading to the clover field. At the hive entrance the continuous roar of fanners can be heard. The flow is on.

During a flow almost all other hive activity is subordinated to the harvest: guard bees are less vigilant; the egg laying of the queen is reduced; nurse bees are released for more urgent tasks. As the store grows, more comb may have to be built to accommodate it. A hive can grow ten pounds heavier in a single day during such a nectar flow. A change in weather may bring the flow to an end after a few days, or it may continue for several weeks, until the plants themselves are exhausted. Often the cessation, like the beginning, is quite sudden. If it is still early in the season, the foragers who have worn themselves out and died will be replaced by another force, ready for the flow from some other plant; but if summer is coming to an end, and the queen's laying has diminished, then the population will decline. With full combs of precious honey in the hive, and little nectar to be had outside, the guard bees will be very alert. The would-be intruder had better be careful. Although bees can be very aggressive in protecting their stores in the hive, there seems to be no antagonism in the field, even between bees of different species. If one arrives at a flower already occupied by another, it simply turns off to seek nectar elsewhere. On composite flowers with large heads, it is not uncommon to see two or more bees on the same head, apparently indifferent to each other's presence.

If spring is the urgent season for the honeybee, then summer is surely the busiest. Through sheer physical exertion, summer workers live for a shorter period than workers of any other season. They are sacrificed to the future well-being of their organism and the spread of the species.

Fall and Winter

The earth is baked hard, and the great summer abundance of flowers is gone. Now is the time of fruits and seeds. Since the last of the nectar flows, the bee colony had declined in numbers and the foragers no longer stream from the hive. Activity has not ceased entirely, for there are still the fall flowers, which at least provide day-to-day rations of nectar and contribute to the pollen stores. Internally the hive is being prepared for the hard months ahead. Unripe honey will be brought in from the more remote combs, to be finished and stored near the brood nest. Pollen is covered with honey for preservation and sealed over with wax. Guard bees are now particularly on the alert to protect the hard-won stores against robbers. Until the really cold nights come, the queen will still be laying eggs, though a steadily decreasing number, so that there shall be nurse bees available for the great awakening next spring. The brood nest will now be very compact, for all is to be arranged to the best advantage of the winter cluster.

This is the time of year when large quantities of propolis are brought in and used. Throughout the season a certain amount of this brown sticky substance is gathered. Combs are strengthened with propolis varnish, which partly accounts for their darkening with age. The interior surfaces of the hive also receive a coating, and cracks and holes, other than the hive entrance, are filled with a mixture of wax and propolis during these last active weeks when the material is abundant.

Within the bodies of the bees themselves there are physiological preparations for the coming winter. Insects have tissues known as fat-bodies, mainly in the abdomen, that act as internal food reserves. The hibernating queens of wasps and bumblebees live entirely on such reserves during the winter. Worker honeybees resulting from the late summer and early fall egg laying by the queen also have these tissues well developed, much more than do the earlier generations. The activity of workers in the height of the season is so intense, and their lives so short, that there is no chance for bodily reserves to build up. At the end of the season circumstances are different; there is less and less for these late bees to do. Nevertheless, like all young workers, they do consume large amounts of pollen. Even though there is no larva feeding for them to do, the brood-feed glands develop, and surplus becomes incorporated in their fat-bodies. This reserve, together with low activity, accounts for the longevity of the winter bees compared with the summer ones. They remain young bees for several months and do not begin to age until brood raising starts again, a task they are ready to begin before nectar and pollen become available from outside the hive. This is one secret in the bees' approach to winter; another lies in subtle adaptations of the clustering habit.

Winter clustering begins when the temperature in the hive drops below 57 degrees; the lower the temperature, the more compact the cluster. Its form is roughly spherical, depending somewhat on the shape of the nest cavity and the number of combs present. The bulk of the cluster is on empty comb, with its edges in contact with food stores. As food is consumed, the cluster slowly moves in an upward direction, although it will move sideways if the food is in that direction. Small groups of bees on the outer faces of combs running through the cluster are not isolated from the rest. Contact is always maintained at one edge or another. The outer shell, which may be several layers of bees thick, consists of quiescent bees close together, with their heads turned inward, some right inside the cells. Within this insulating shell there is room for movement and comparative activity.

A bee, because it is cold-blooded, becomes less active as the temperature of its surroundings goes down. A critical point is reached if the bee's body temperature drops to 46°. Below this temperature the bee could no longer cling to its fellows; it would fall from the cluster and die. To insure the necessary warmth, the colony as a whole has a self-regulating mechanism. The superorganism is in a sense a warm-blooded animal.

Heat is generated in the thorax of the bee through its consumption of honey, which promotes muscular vibrations. A certain amount of movement by individuals and the usual food transmission process insure that all get a share of food and heat. Because of the live insulation on the outside of the cluster, the inside temperature is always high, seldom below 68 and sometimes rising to 96. Heat radiated from the center to the bees on the outside keeps those bees above the critical minimum.

Obviously such regulation of heat affects the amount of food consumed, and in prolonged cold weather the stores may not last. The bees have other methods of conservation; efficient wintering depends in large part on mechanical control of the cluster. Its outer shell can be varied in density, thus controlling its effectiveness as an insulating layer; and the number of bees in the center can be regulated. Most important of all, though, is the changing of the cluster's diameter. Mathematically-oriented readers know that a comparatively small decrease in the diameter of a sphere causes a large reduction in surface area. Fewer bees on a smaller surface will radiate less heat, with a consequent saving in the food consumed by the whole organism. The process is automatic; the bees on the outside as they approach the critical temperature try to squeeze in, and the pressure stimulates the necessary adjustment. It is in the most severe weather that the internal temperature of the cluster rises to its maximum and, paradoxical as it may seem, creates a condition in which brood raising may begin.

The picture shouldn't be oversimplified; there is still the question of waste products. Carbon dioxide and water result from the combustion of sugar, and neither of these substances can be allowed to accumulate in the hive. Some of the water can be retained in the digestive system for a time, but most of it must be evaporated and removed by ventilation. The carbon dioxide must also be disposed of this way. There must be an air flow through the cluster sufficient to carry these waste gases right out of the hive. The more honey that is consumed, the more gases there will be, and the more air required to remove them. The regulation of cluster density also affects this. Of course the moving airstream takes away some of the valuable heat, but the bees instinctively maintain the right balance.

It is believed that bees are better able to survive a cold, dry winter climate than a mild but excessively damp one. Within certain limitations, cold by itself does not kill them; their central heating system, with its automatic regulation, will get them by, provided there is sufficient food. In parts of Canada, for instance, where there is an abundance of nectar-producing flowers in the short, hot summer, bees will store enough to live through weeks of sub-zero temperatures in the winter. But one poor summer can doom practically all wild colonies, and several years may elapse before the bee population builds up again.

When temperatures do not go extremely low, but where for most of the winter months the air entering the hive is already saturated with water vapor, the situation is quite different. Even so, the cluster adjusts itself to meet the circumstances. The only way in which such air can be made to take up more water vapor is for its temperature to be raised, and then the effect is slight. So the bees arrange the cluster to allow a relatively large amount of air to flow through it, warming up and taking water vapor as it goes. Condensation of the vapor on hive walls will often aggravate the condition, but bees in hundreds of such circumstances manage to survive. It can be seen now why swarms instinctively avoid both damp and windy places. A strong current of air blowing across the entrance to a hive makes it more difficult for the bees to control the internal conditions during the winter and is always a disadvantage to foragers in the summer. Nevertheless, in the dampness of winter in Great Britain, or the cold dryness of Canada, the honeybee gives proof of its wonderful adaptability.

The bees keep themselves warm, but they do not heat the inside of the hive. The temperature only a few inches from the cluster will be about the same as outside. The hive does act as a buffer against rapid changes of temperature that would disturb the cluster, and more important, it gives protection against wind and rain. In the cluster itself the combs have good insulating value, especially if full of honey. The strong, well-provided colony has every possible advantage; it is easier for a large number of bees to maintain optimum heat production and ventilation than it is for a small number and food consumption will be proportionately less. The amount of food needed to see a colony through until the flowers bloom again varies greatly, according to local circumstances. Anywhere from twenty-five to fifty pounds may be regarded as a minimum.

The honeybee then is not a true hibernator; there is some activity during the winter, but it is minimal, and so controlled as to make the best possible use of resources and insure that the maximum number of individuals shall survive to start the next annual cycle. There can be breaking of the cluster and even a cleansing flight during the winter. Such flights occur more frequently after the new year. Not only do the opportunities arise more often at that time, but also pollen is being consumed by the nurse bees, and the amount of waste is consequently increasing.

The resumption of brood raising in the winter cluster as the temperature rises in the center, brings the queen's period of rest to an end. She begins to receive more royal jelly from the workers, and her dormant ovaries come into

In the winter a cleansing flight is made.

operation once more, slowly at first, but gradually developing so that she is in full lay by the time the warm days come. The honeybees' wintering system allows them to anticipate spring many weeks before it arrives. When it does come, there are already hundreds of new foragers to serve Nature's purpose in pollinating the fruit blossoms and other early flowers, and the colonies themselves are way ahead in their drive for summer prosperity.

9. the bees' enemies

Having learned to produce honey for herself, the bee had to contend with her enemies. Many other creatures craved the sweet food and were prepared to take risks to get it. Apart from man, there are few who can destroy the whole colony and its nest, for the bees have a well-developed system of defense. But robbers that can brave the stings are serious enemies.

Bears are in this category. They not only have a great liking for honey, but also enjoy eating the larvae in the combs. The large ones are strong enough to tear open a tree containing a nest, and they seldom leave a thing. The bees attack them on the tender part of the face, the only part that is vulnerable to the stings, but bears will put up with a good deal of pain for such a prize. In sections of the United States and Canada, bears are often a serious menace to commercial bee-keeping. Hives made of wooden boxes, standing on the ground, are easily invaded, and a large number in one place must be a bear's idea of heaven. To protect apiaries, stockades have been built, but these are expensive. Hunting for bears is now restricted in some parts by wildlife conservation laws, but the electric fence, similar to that used for cattle, has proved quite an effective deterrent.

As much a menace as large bears are tiny ants, who can be very persistent robbers. They can enter a hive through minute crevices that the bees have not sealed, or elude the guards at a larger aperture. By crawling up the hive sides away from the combs, they may be able to reach honey in areas momentarily unoccupied by the bees. Ants, too, have a system of communication, based on scent trails left by their foragers. Once a few of them have succeeded in stealing honey from a hive, others will soon follow. At the first sign of a mass invasion, the bees will be alerted. The battle may be a long one, lasting for days, even weeks. The bees are unable to use their stings effectively on a creature so small, and they rely on biting and mauling. Injured ants will be thrown out by the hundreds. On the other hand, a large mass of ants can so smother a bee, biting at its wings and other body parts, that it falls a victim, to be pulled out of the hive and eaten by the omnivorous raiders. In hot climates such ant attacks can seriously deplete a colony of bees, but in temperate zones the bees usually keep the ants in check and suffer little material loss. Even so, ants are a nuisance. And in hot climates, termites, as well as some ant species, will eat away the wood parts of domestic hives.

The wasp is more than a match for a single bee, but the guard bees come quickly to the rescue.

Toward the close of summer, wasps will make determined efforts to rob hives. These are formidable opponents—strong, alert, active on the wing, and with very powerful jaws. Wasps, like ants, are social insects and can organize mass attacks. Bee guards at this time are ever on the alert for raiding wasps, and many individual battles take place. A wasp is more than a match for a single bee, but the defender usually gets help quickly. Either insect can use its sting effectively against the other, and does, but the wasp uses its mandibles as well, and is quite capable of severing a bee's head from its body in one movement. While a fight is going on between one or two wasps and the guard bees, another wasp may slip into the hive unnoticed. If it succeeds in getting out again with stolen sweets, it will try again later and bring others with it. The battle will then intensify, and the whole colony is alerted. Victims will fall by the hundreds to the ground below the hive entrance. A strong healthy colony of bees will triumph over the wasps; its losses are mainly among those bees that had not long to live anyway. A weak colony may lose the battle and be completely destroyed.

Although not a serious menace to colonies, there is a solitary predatory wasp—one of the digger wasps, *Philanthus triangulum*—that specializes in the honeybee as a victim. Like other members of that family, this one digs a branched hole in sandy soil to form a nest in which it will lay eggs. The larvae develop, each having been provided with a paralyzed body on which to feed—in this case, that of a honeybee. By a series of cunning moves, the wasp is able to grasp the bee while it is foraging on a flower, and hold it in such a way that it can insert its sting under the bee's chin. This action not only paralyzes the bee, which provides fresh meat for the wasp larva, but at the same time causes it to regurgitate any nectar in its honey sac, and so provide food for the adult wasp too.

There are many creatures that like the bees themselves as food—insectivores that range from spiders to birds to skunks. A spider may spin a web against a hive entrance to trap her dinner. Dragonflies pounce on bees when both are in flight. When a hive is close to the ground, a toad will often take up residence and provide himself with regular meals as the bees fly in and out. Lizards adopt the same method, but the bees do not seem to be conscious of their presence and seldom attack them. There are many kinds of birds that will take bees on the wing, but from most of them the loss of bees is small. However, there are a few that are particularly fond of the honeybee and have learned to locate hives; they present a more serious threat. Kingbirds in parts of the United States are such birds. In North Africa there is the bee eater, whose depredations make bee-keeping in some areas very difficult. These birds, who subsist solely on bees, fly up and down along the lines of bee flight near the hives and catch the insects on the wing. In proportion to hive population, losses seem slight; but colonies can become so weakened that they eventually succumb to attacks by other enemies.

There are other birds that take a toll of the hives in winter and early spring. During one winter I watched a pair of great tits that spent a lot of their time

The long-tailed tit is a common bee-eating bird in Europe.

perched on the roof of one of my hives. If the weather was mild and the bees slightly active, any bee that ventured from the entrance was immediately snapped up by one of the pair. On colder days the birds had to work harder for their food. They would go down to the entrance and tap about with their beaks. Sooner or later a bee or two from the disturbed cluster would come to the entrance to investigate, and meet with an untimely death. This went on for many weeks, and by spring the colony was very weak indeed, although it survived. Since then, I have draped string netting over any hive being so attacked; this keeps the birds away from the entrance, as their feet are liable to get tangled in the netting.

Also in the British Isles, the green woodpecker has, during the last thirty years or so, acquired the habit of attacking man-made hives during the winter, and feeding on the bees inside if it reaches them. It will peck holes several inches in diameter in the sides or near the entrances of the hives, spending some days on the job. Again, any curious bees get snapped up. Eventually colonies become very depleted. Whether this bird ever attacks wild bee's nests is not known, but its normal diet consists of insects found under the bark of trees, so it is not improbable. None of the older books mentions the green woodpecker as an enemy of the bee, and apparently this bird has learned to recognize our beehives quite recently.

Mice may not be deliberate enemies. It is possible that their main purpose in entering hives during the winter is for shelter. (The bees being clustered and quiescent are not apt to molest them; during the active season such invaders would be stung to death.) Once inside, the mice will eat honey and pollen from unoccupied combs and destroy them as they do so. Sometimes a mouse squeezes itself into a narrow hive entrance, and then so gorges itself on honey and wax that it is too fat to get out again, and dies of thirst. Apart from the loss of food, the actual disturbance caused by mice in the hive is bad for the bees; a colony that has housed a mouse in winter will usually be very weak in the spring, even

Mice, if they find their way into the hive, can cause a great deal of damage. On this mouse-eaten comb, a wasp's nest is being started.

if it has enough food left to survive. Narrowing the hive entrances before the onset of winter, to prevent entry of mice, is standard practice among beekeepers almost everywhere.

In the United States, skunks will make regular visits to beehives and consume large numbers of the inmates as they fly out. They also disturb the colony by scratching outside and catching their victims as they show themselves, in the same way birds do.

It is doubtful if wax moths do much harm to natural colonies of bees. They act as scavengers in nests that have been abandoned and in hives where the inmates have died out. In commercial beekeeping, where the practice is to store empty combs for use in the following season, wax moths can be a serious problem, and preventive measures have to be taken. There are two common species, both pale gray, with few distinctive markings. The greater wax moth, *Galleria melonella*, measuring about one and a half inches across the wing tips, is far more troublesome than the lesser wax moth, *Achroia grisella*, which is less than half that size. Their life histories are very similar, and as is usual with moths, it is the larvae that do the damage.

The females lay their eggs in crevices adjacent to the combs, into which the hatching larvae burrow. It is not just the wax that forms their diet, but also such things as pollen remains and bee pupa skins, which contain protein. As the larvae feed they tunnel through the combs and destroy them, leaving only a tangled weblike debris, and skins that they themselves have molted. The life cycle varies from one month to several, depending on temperature conditions and the food value of the combs. They spend a long time working on clean new comb, and often eat into surrounding wood to supplement their diet. During the winter months eggs and larvae can lie dormant in places where they do not actually freeze.

The moths also enter occupied hives, mostly in the late evening when few guard bees are active. They never approach the entrance directly, but with quick and skillful flight from one side, they dart in unobserved. If not successful at first, they approach from the opposite side a few moments later. They can run unusually fast for moths, and once inside they soon scamper out of the bees' reach to await the opportunity to lay their eggs. Bees do not tolerate the larvae in the combs they are using, and will remove all they can get at, but unoccupied combs may be badly damaged.

The obvious protection a beekeeper can give his spare combs is to pack them away in a mothproof place. This is not always easy in the busy season, for moth eggs may be in them before he has tended to this. He often resorts to chemicals. There are a number of fumigants that give effective control, but the best of them, such as carbon disulfide and calcium cyanide, are rather dangerous to handle. Paradichlorobenzene is safe, and quite good if the combs are packed in a fairly airtight space and if the crystals are replaced when they have volatilized.

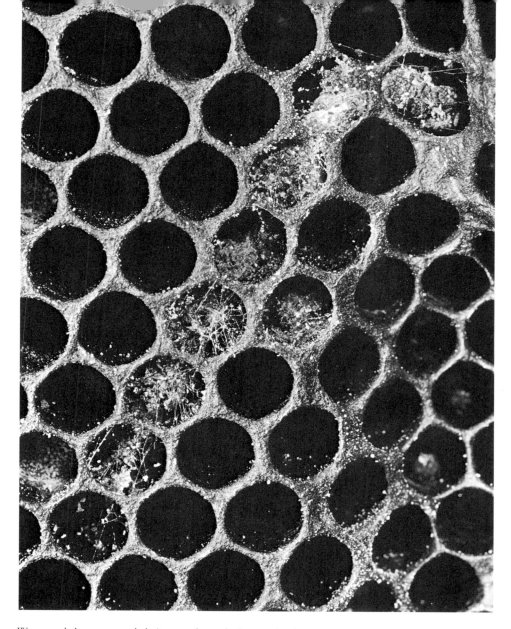

Wax moth larvae tunnel their way through the combs, leaving a tangle of debris behind them.

Like any other living thing, the honeybee has its share of parasites and diseases. One parasite, the bee louse, *Braula coeca*, is more often found on queens than on workers. A queen may have a great number of them clustered round her neck, and being a reddish color, they resemble a coral necklace. They do not feed on the body of the queen itself, but lick at the edges of her mouth and share the food she receives from the nurse bees. The lavish feeding of the queen makes her the preferred host. These bee lice occur locally, more likely in warm districts than cold, and they are not regarded as a serious menace to the bees.

In Europe, an eight-legged parasite called the acarine mite sometimes enters the breathing spiracles of a bee's thorax. Multiplying in the tubes within, restricting the breathing of the host and feeding on its tissues, it considerably shortens the bee's life. In a bad attack, the whole colony is handicapped, and there have been times when the activities of this pest have reached epidemic dimensions. So far, in spite of prolonged search, the acarine mite has not been found in the United States, at least not in this form. It seems hardly possible that not one has ever reached America; perhaps it has adopted a different host or changed its way of life. However, what appears to be a harmless relative of the acarine mite has been found in very small numbers, and exists only externally on the bee.

A much more serious parasite everywhere is the microscopic organism *Nosema apis*, which lives in the digestive tract of any of the bees. At times it seriously reduces the strength and potential of colonies, and in very bad cases, causes them to die outright. Nosema is found in every country where bees thrive, and it is probable that most colonies house a few individuals that are affected by it. In certain circumstances, particularly when bees have been confined to the hive for long periods, the infection can spread rapidly. Among beekeepers, losses from nosema have been heavy in Europe; the United States has not suffered quite so much.

There is a rhythm in the progress of nosema within a colony because of the way it is transmitted from one bee to another. Spores of the organism are passed in the excrement of an infected bee. During the winter, unable to make a cleansing flight, these sick bees become dysenteric and soil the inside of the hive. When spring activity commences, healthy bees start to clean up the combs and become infected themselves. The number of diseased bees increases rapidly, and the colony dwindles. However, once the weather is good enough for free flying, the rate of infection drops and the hive recovers. If a good season follows, all the combs are cleaned up, and the trouble may not recur to any serious extent next spring. In a poor season the recovery is less complete, and the trouble may be worse next time.

Of the bacterial diseases specifically affecting the honeybee, the two most common attack the larvae. They are American foul brood and European foul brood (AFB and EFB for short). The names have no significance whatever; both occur in the New World and in the Old. American bees came from Europe, anyway, and must have brought these diseases with them. They were known in ancient times and were both referred to simply as 'stinking brood.' An unpleasant smell exuding from the dead larvae at a certain stage of putrefaction is, as the name suggests, a common factor. The distinction between the two did not come until life in the hive could be observed more closely, and then finally with the study of causal organisms from 1874 onward. Both diseases are bacterial in origin and spread from spores left in dead larvae, but the age and manner of the death they cause differs, as does the cycle of the disease in the colony as a whole.

Under natural conditions AFB is the more serious, for, once infected, the colony is almost bound to die. The bees appear to have very little resistance to it, although some strains seem more immune than others. The larva dies in the prepupal stage, just after its cell is sealed. The capping sinks and becomes perforated. The bees eventually remove the capping and try to remove the corpse from the cell, but they are unable to do so because the skin has become very tough and firmly attached to the comb. It contains a coffee-colored, glutinous mass, which at a certain stage can be drawn out on the end of a matchstick in a thread about two inches long. Finally it dries up into a hard brown scale, lying lengthwise in the bottom of the cell, and remains there. The scale contains millions of the disease spores. No egg will be laid in that cell again, but food will be stored in it. The food naturally becomes contaminated, and when it is fed to future larvae, they get infected with the disease. For some unknown reason only worker larvae succumb to AFB. A colony that dies out from this cause may be robbed of its stores by another colony; in this way the disease is spread. The spores can remain viable for years and will even survive boiling in water and treatment with powerful chemicals. AFB would appear to be a disease that might well have wiped out the honeybee species. Perhaps in this respect the wax moth has been its savior. By completely destroying the combs left by dead colonies, the wax moth halts the spread of the disease.

EFB is rarely directly fatal to the colony as a whole, for it is active for a limited season only—usually in May and early June—and the bees are able to combat it to some extent. It has a weakening effect, and lowers the honey-gathering potential. Therefore, a colony might die from starvation the following winter. With EFB it is the younger larvae that are the sufferers, for they die before reaching the sealing stage, and queen and drone larvae may be affected, as well as workers. The bodies lie contorted in the open cells and are usually removed before long by the bees. However slightly or severely a colony may be affected, the disease always clears up by the end of the season. But despite the removal of the corpses, spores evidently remain in the combs, or somewhere, for once infected, a colony is liable to catch the disease in succeeding seasons, often more severely. EFB still poses some mysteries to scientists; it is a long way from being fully understood. Although the bacillus causing the primary infection is known, there are secondary invaders, and the course of the disease is not constant.

Wherever man brings together large numbers of a single species of plant or animal for his own purposes, he creates conditions in which the species' natural enemies and diseases can flourish. He then has to fight a continuous battle to maintain healthy and profitable stock. The diseases mentioned in this chapter are probably rarely disastrous to bees in a wild state; but where we keep large numbers of colonies close together, troubles can always arise, and beekeepers have to be vigilant. The governments of most countries where bees are kept on a commercial scale have had to introduce legislation to protect against the foul brood diseases. This usually requires state inspection and the destruction of all colonies found to be infected. Such destruction includes the burning of all combs, for these are considered to be the main source of infection. Fortunately there are now antibiotics that offer at least some control over foul brood and nosema.

Following the dramatic success of the sulfa drugs in the treatment of human diseases, veterinary researchers in many countries began using these drugs on farm animals. In 1944 two American scientists, Haseman and Childers, announced some success in the control of AFB by feeding bee colonies sugar syrup containing sulfathiazole, a drug now widely used for this purpose. It does not actually kill the spores, but it inhibits their growth and is a preventive rather than a curative treatment. EFB responds similarly to the antibiotic Terramycin; and because of the seasonal nature of the disease, the control seems to be even more effective. Much success in the control of nosema has been achieved with another antibiotic, Fumagillin. This substance, with sugar, is fed to the bees in fall and spring; it is a particularly effective cure if the bees are induced to build new combs to replace the old and possibly infected ones.

Any discussion on pests and diseases tends to produce a pessimistic view as to the victim's prospects. It should be remembered that the normal condition of all living things is a healthy one, and this certainly applies to bees. Few colonies suffer severely from the troubles mentioned in this chapter, even those kept intensively by man. They do, however, run further risks, arising from the use of poisonous chemicals to control crop pests and weeds on farmland. This is discussed in the next chapter.

10. bees and man

Early man was a honey robber, an enemy of the bee. Today he is a honey producer who cares for his bees as valuable stock. He has spread them to parts of the world they could never have reached on their own, and maintains them in much greater numbers than nature could provide. Even a skillful collector from wild nests might gather no more than one hundred pounds of honey in a season, and that only with much work and considerable pain. Today a commercial beekeeper measures his crop in tons. He keeps several hundred, perhaps a thousand or more, colonies completely under his control, taking them to places where nectar is abundant. In the United States he would regard one hundred pounds from each colony as a minimum paying crop.

For every commercial beekeeper there are probably a hundred others who keep a small number of colonies. These are mainly hobbyists, who keep bees for the pleasure and interest they get from them. In the aggregate these colonies produce a lot of honey, and as they are widely spread, the pollination service rendered by their bee colonies has a national value. To a person of the right temperament, living in a suitable situation, beekeeping is both an absorbing and a relaxing hobby.

In addition to honey, beeswax, obtained by melting down the honeycombs, is a valuable product of the hive. In its bleached form, large quantities are still used in the cosmetic and pharmaceutical industries. Church candles, particularly those used in Roman Catholic churches, contain a large proportion of beeswax, the candle's clean flame being regarded as a symbol of purity. Although substitutes for beeswax have been found for the manufacture of domestic polishes, there are many minor uses for it in industry, and the demand for beeswax throughout the world is considerable. A high proportion of the wax appearing on the market is gathered from wild bees' nests in Africa.

There is abundant archaeological evidence that honey and wax production was an important industry in all the ancient civilizations of the Middle East. The bee was sacred in Egypt, and temple carvings depict bees and beekeeping scenes. The great writers of Greece and Rome gave instruction in bee husbandry, mixed with mythological stories of its natural history. Pliny was one of these, and some of his instructions remain sound practice today; but, like his contemporaries, he had fanciful notions of the nature of the bee and its world. For instance, he repeats the old Greek myth about spontaneous generation of bees from the decaying carcasses of oxen. The Bible story of Samson and the lion is similar and older. Both probably arise through confusing the bee with the drone fly, which it resembles superficially. Pliny says that 'honey is engendered from the air, mostly at the rising of the constellations, and more especially when Sirius is shining,' and extends the notion by saying that when gathered just after the appearance of a rainbow it is a heavenly nostrum, with powers to cure many diseases.

In practical beekeeping some progress was made in Roman times. They learned to feed starving colonies with a sugary liquid obtained by soaking pulped raisins and dried figs in water, to which they added wine. For a long time bees have been fed, when necessary, with cane sugar syrup, and until about a hundred years ago, beekeepers in England still followed the Roman example by adding beer to the syrup. The Romans also put extensions above or below their hives during a honey flow, a practice every beekeeper follows today. They must have been successful, for Varro mentions an apiary near Naples that produced five thousand pounds of honey a year, and the islands of Corsica and Cyprus paid taxes to the central government in honey and beeswax.

Although the most exciting chapters in our knowledge of the bee and its ways have been written in the last few hundred years, beekeeping as a craft goes back a long way. Long before written history, men had made two important discoveries: Bees could be subdued and handled by the use of smoke; and swarms could be readily taken when clustered, and established in places of man's choosing. We shall never know who found out these things—whether they happened in one place, and the knowledge spread slowly across Asia and Europe over thousands of years, or whether they occurred independently in several places.

All creatures whose natural homes are in wooded land have an inborn fear of the forest fire and instinctively flee before it. Bees react quickly to the smell of smoke in the hive. Many rush to the honey cells and gorge themselves on the contents, perhaps as a first stage in preparing to leave home. As a full bee is less inclined to sting, the whole colony loses its normal alertness and becomes subdued. The beekeeper makes good use of this knowledge. By smoking a hive it is possible to open it and work in it, without getting badly stung—often without being stung at all. The antiquity of this discovery is shown in the prehistoric painting mentioned in Chapter 1, where the honey-gatherer is portrayed carrying a smoldering torch. Today an appliance for producing smoke is a fundamental tool for the beekeeper.

This last discovery could have been made by observation; the other one would seem more difficult. A swarm that has left its hive and settled on a bush or tree can be dislodged by a vigorous shake and made to fall into a suitable recep-

A beekeeper may carry a clustered swarm to a more convenient site such as a straw skep.

tacle, then be carried off by the new owner to a convenient site. If the container is also suitable for the bees to nest in, they may be left in it; otherwise, something having the right type of cavity may be placed on the ground, and the bees shaken before it. As soon as a few bees have found their way into the dark space the swarm will run in. Nearly always it will accept this as a new home, for in the handling of the bees, communication between the searchers, who have been looking for a nesting place, has been broken. Rarely can bees be handled so easily, and without provoking retaliation, as in a swarm. Being gorged with food makes them quiescent; besides, they have neither a home nor brood to defend.

Think what this discovery meant to our ancestors. Instead of having to search miles for bees' nests, they could place hollow tree logs close to their dwellings and establish swarms in them. A supply of honey would be available from the home apiary. Man thus became a beekeeper.

Such beekeeping followed a simple pattern. Watch would be kept during the swarming season so that emerging swarms could be taken and hived. At the end of the season certain colonies would be chosen to remain as next year's stock, and honey would be taken from the others. This kind of beekeeping went on for thousands of years and is still practiced in many parts of the world.

If a hollow log was the first thing used to house bees, human ingenuity soon devised other hives. It was indeed necessary, for in many places where beekeeping was widely practiced, trees were not plentiful. Hives woven of wood, rushes, or straw had the advantage of being easily portable. Baked-earthenware hives, common in the Mediterranean countries, are still found in North Africa. The poor European peasant in the Middle Ages saved wheat straw, and during the winter he would wind this into rope, which he coiled into the domed basketlike skep hives. All over northern Europe (the size and shape varied locally) this hive was in general use, until the appearance of the modern movable comb hive constructed of wood. The skep was cheap, easily made, and ideal for the climate, and it has not yet entirely disappeared.

Beekeeping was an important industry in Europe throughout the Middle Ages, for honey was the only sweetening agent available for home use. Sugarcane, discovered in India in the fourteenth century, was not planted in southern Europe until a century later. At least another hundred years elapsed before cane sugar came to the northern countries in any large quantities, but it was expensive. Beeswax, too, had its traditional uses, especially for altar candles as the power of the church grew and the great monasteries and cathedrals were built. Many a peasant farmer paid his church dues in beeswax. Nevertheless, little progress seems to have been made in the craft of beekeeping during this time.

The scientific and technical age was dawning in the sixteenth century. Observation and experiment were taking the place of tradition and fable, and the new thirst for knowledge extended into every field of human activity. In beekeeping there came a desire both to learn more of the life within the hive and to improve practical management. An immensely important discovery was made in 1586 by Luis Mendez de Torres, a Spaniard. Up to this time the large and obviously important individual that appeared in every swarm had always been known as the king bee. De Torres, however, had observed this bee laying eggs and therefore pronounced it female. This revelation was soon followed by another. Charles Butler in England, in his book *Feminine Monarchie*, published in 1609, not only confirmed the queen as a female, but also established the drones as male bees. The Dutch naturalist Jan Swammerdam, that early genius with the microscope, who lived from 1637 to 1680, proved the sex of both queen and workers by dissection.

The eighteenth century saw renewed interest. The first account of the mating of queens and drones was given by Anton Janscha, a Slovene, in 1771. He was also successful in inducing bees to raise queens in small pieces of comb containing young larvae. The blind Swiss naturalist François Huber, through the eyes of his manservant, made a lifelong study of life within the hive. His book, published in 1792, gave the most complete story of bee life told up to that time. He also included details for the controlled raising of queens.

Huber's success was due largely to his invention of a hive that permitted separate combs to be examined at any time, without damage and with minimum disturbance to the bees. It consisted of a number of wooden frames of the same size, so constructed that one edge of each was hinged to its neighbor on either side. When a small strip of comb was put in a frame, the bees were persuaded to extend it until the area inside was completely filled. The frames were placed together, face to face, so that the combs were arranged as in a natural nest, but the hinges allowed any one to be examined at will by prising apart and opening them as one would the leaves of a book. This, the first movable comb hive, was a splendid tool for observation purposes, though it had some drawbacks for practical honey production.

Already there were many people using wood-box hives as an alternative to the straw skep. The principle of stacking the boxes to vary the capacity was well established. To have combs that could be removed individually at will would give the beekeeper tremendous advantages in the control and management of his stock. Many attempts were made to find a satisfactory design. A hive with separate comb frames, all contained in a wood casing, was obviously the ideal, but before such an arrangement could be perfected there was a problem to be solved. So far, the frames were fitted into a hive, and however well the idea worked at first, there came a time when the frames were firmly glued to the body of the hive—and probably to each other. The bees had cemented them with propolis! It was impossible to remove any without breaking them. The nature of the bee did not seem to fit in with human schemes.

The answer came from the Reverend Lorenzo L. Langstroth of Andover, Massachusetts, a keen naturalist and beekeeper and a born experimenter. He made

The basic hive now in common use holds separate comb frames that can be removed for examination. The beekeeper has driven the bees down with smoke and has opened the hive from the top. He removes the top, then a single frame. New comb fills the frame.

hives based on a European design, with the combs attached to wood bars across the top of each box section. This facilitated stacking the boxes for honey storage. In 1851 he noticed that if the bottoms of the combs in one box had a space of about three-eighths of an inch between them and the bars of the box below, the bees did not fill the space. This simplified the removal of the upper box. Langstroth remembered that bees in a natural nest frequently leave passageways around combs to let them travel easily about the hive. He now built hives incorporating this bee-space idea throughout. The comb frames hung by their top bars, which rested on recessed edges of the hive box; at each side and on top was a space measuring one-quarter to three-eighths of an inch. Bees could pass around the ends of these frames, as well as between them when one lot was above another. It worked; the bees respected these spaces, filling them neither with propolis nor with comb. A completely workable hive was now available, and a new chapter in beekeeping was opened.

Bees often leave passageways around the comb. The artificial hive incorporates similar 'bee space' between the hive wall and the sides of the frames.

The first edition of Langstroth's book *The Hive and the Honey Bee*, was published in 1853. In it he describes his hive with modest reference to his discovery of the bee space. More than that, he gives details of the possibilities in bee management, now that a truly movable and interchangeable comb hive could be made. Colonies could be divided at will, swarming controlled, and the bees induced to raise queens at the discretion of the beekeeper. Any desired number of hive boxes could be added at any time and readily removed. The new idea caught on quickly in America, and large-scale honey production was soon on the way. The book was translated into several languages, and spread the new method across the world. Nearly all hives used in the major honey-producing countries at the present time are still made to his original basic measurements and are called Langstroth hives. There has, however, been a general simplification of the first design. Elsewhere there are many different sizes and patterns of hive, but all now incorporate the bee-space principle.

Other important inventions soon followed. It was not always easy to get the bees to build straight combs accurately within the frames. In 1857 Johannes Mehring, in Germany, succeeded in pressing out sheets of beeswax with comb cell impressions on them. These sheets, fixed inside the frames, were accepted by the bees as a foundation, and good combs were quickly built. Today all bee-keepers use comb foundation, which is now produced in roller mills.

Also needed was a more efficient way of extracting honey from the combs. Methods so far in use, such as pressing it out through woven bags, were slow and messy, and always resulted in the destruction of the combs. True, beeswax had a good market value, but the combs as such were more valuable to the beekeeper. The bees would use them over and over again, as they did in nature. A machine that would remove honey from the combs by centrifugal force, without damaging them, was invented by an Austrian, Major F. Hruschka, in 1865. The modern power-driven honey extractor can handle large quantities in a short time.

The queen excluder is another piece of modern equipment. It consists of either a sheet of perforated metal or spaced wires in a frame, with gaps large enough to permit the passage of workers, but too small to admit the thorax of a queen. Thus the queen can be confined to the lower boxes of the hive, leaving her room to lay eggs, while the upper ones are free for the bees to store honey. Its use simplifies the removal of the honey crop by insuring that no brood is taken with it.

Both Huber and Janscha had succeeded in raising new queens by supplying queenless bees with young larvae in pieces of comb. Janscha, a very practical beekeeper, also made use of a temporary caging method in introducing a young mated queen to strange bees. The advantages in having extra queens available are evident. If a beekeeper divides a colony artificially, either to increase his stock or to control the swarming instinct, the queenless portion can be given a laying queen immediately. Growth proceeds; there is no waste of valuable summer weeks waiting for one to be reared and mated. No modern beekeeper allows a queen to get so old that her egg-laying powers fail; he will replace her before that. Some commercial men believe that it pays to requeen every year.

Many methods have been devised for producing queen cells in large numbers at times convenient to the beekeeper. The most popular today are based on a system published by an American, G. M. Doolittle, in 1882. Artificial queen cell cups are made by dipping rounded sticks of wood into molten beeswax. After several dippings and cooling, the cells are pulled off the sticks and a dozen or so are stuck in a row on a bar of wood that fits into a comb frame. Several such bars may be prepared for one hive. Next, a comb containing larvae less than thirty-six hours old is taken from the hive of a selected breeder queen. With a special tool the larvae are skillfully lifted out, and one is gently placed in each of the artificial cups. It has to be done quickly and in the right conditions of temperature and humidity. From there, the bars are put into a hive that has been prepared to receive them. It will be queenless, strong in young bees, and with an abundance of food, but containing no other larvae young enough to make into queens. In this way it is possible to get large numbers of well-fed young queens. The bees extend the artificial cups to finish the cells off in the usual way, but in subsequent operations these cells are more readily handled by the beekeeper than entirely natural ones.

Of course, the cells must be removed from the building colony before any queen emerges, for she would probably destroy all the rest. The beekeeper has already placed small lots of queenless bees in what he calls nucleus hives. Each of these will receive a ripe queen cell, and in due course the virgins are mated. Once in lay, the queens are available for use elsewhere, and the nuclei may receive a fresh batch of cells. Large-scale queen raising is a specialized business in localities where the honey seasons are early and the weather dependable. Such conditions exist in the southern section of the United States, and in Italy. From these places, queens are mailed in cages to beekeepers everywhere.

The queen-raisers in the United States have also developed the package-bee business: not only queens but also large numbers of workers are produced by them early in the year. These are shaken into cages holding two-pound or three-pound lots, with a queen for each, and shipped to places farther north, where they will be used to start new colonies. A fair number of these packages have been flown to Europe in the past few years. In Canada and some northern states, where colonies need a lot of food for winter and the risk of loss is high, many beekeepers find it more economical to kill off their bees in the fall and restock with packages the following spring.

In North America about 5,500,000 hives of bees are kept, with an average annual production of some 130,000 tons of honey. Australia and South America also have a considerable honey industry. Russia is by tradition a great beekeeping country, and in the vast area of the U.S.S.R. there are reckoned to be 10,000,000 hives; but the production per hive is less than half that of the United States. This may be due partly to climatic conditions, but the efficient methods of management and mechanical equipment used in the States are not yet in full operation in Russia.

The modern honey producer makes full use of mechanical transport, and moves bees by the truckload to catch the nectar flows as they appear in different areas. In America, trucks are often fitted with devices for easy and rapid loading of the hives. But migratory beekeeping is not new. The beekeepers of ancient Egypt loaded their colonies on rafts and took them to the upper reaches of the Nile as the spring flowers came into bloom. Stage by stage, as the sun came

The author examining a comb.

northward, they moved down the river gathering a succession of honey crops. Today a similar pattern is followed by Australian beekeepers in seeking the vast yields from the eucalyptus trees. They follow the forest blossoms over hundreds of miles of territory, extracting the honey in portable units and sending it to the cities in steel drums.

Great movement of bees also takes place now for the pollination of crops. That many flowers depended on insects for this vital function has been known to naturalists since the middle of the eighteenth century, but it was a long time before the knowledge had any significance for farmers. In the days of small-scale farming and incomplete use of land there were always enough insects to pollinate crops, and nobody paid them much attention. But when large areas were devoted to single crops, the farmers realized that maximum yields from some seed and fruit crops depended on pollinating insects. Efficient farming reduces wild insect populations by destroying their habitats, and pesticides, which are intended for killing harmful insects, destroy many beneficial ones as well. Scientific and field tests have shown that with those plants that the honeybee is able to pollinate, enormous increases in yields, up to 300 percent, can be obtained by moving hives of bees in at blossoming time. More and more growers are becoming aware of this, and part of the commercial beekeeper's income today is derived from renting his bees to growers for pollination. Thousands of hives are taken to orchards and orange groves, and all the leguminous crops that are grown for seed benefit from having hives in the fields. It is fortunate that the honeybee is a good pollinator for so many of our crops, because so far it is the only insect that can be produced in large numbers and kept under complete control. In some places the value of the bee for this work far exceeds that of the honey it produces.

Farmers and beekeepers, working together in this way, face the problem of spray poisoning and its effect on bees. Farming is becoming more and more dependent on the use of chemical substances in the control of pests and weeds. Obviously the powerful insecticides will kill bees, and the herbicides deprive them of much natural forage. Entire apiaries have been wiped out by indiscriminate spraying. Aerial application constitutes by far the greatest danger, for then the material often drifts well beyond the intended area.

In the past, arsenical washes have been the worst for bees. These did not kill only the bees it touched; the foragers drank the poison from the leaves as water and carried it home to the hive, where it killed more bees and brood. Arsenic washes have now been supplanted, but the newer organo-phosphorus and chlorinated hydrocarbon groups are extremely toxic to bees. Phosdrin, sevin, Malathion, and parathion have all been responsible for heavy bee losses. Probably nine-tenths of these have been due to careless or ignorant use of the materials by farmers and spray contractors. Bees die mainly from contact with the poison on open flowers, yet in many instances it is unnecessary or even undesirable to spray at blossom time.

The whole problem of poison sprays is engaging the attention of authorities in many countries, and various acts of legislation are in force to safeguard bees and other innocent sufferers. More of this may come. In the meantime intelligent cooperation between all concerned is needed. Manufacturers try to include bee-repellent substances in their products; farmers must be continually educated in the safe use of chemicals, and warn beekeepers to keep bees out of the area at spraying times. Luckily no trace of any poisonous residues from spray materials has been found in honey so far. Perhaps the best hope for the future lies in the development of chemicals that will be highly specific in their action, or even biological rather than chemical control of pests.

Man, who has made economic use of the bee through the ages, continues to do so in our highly sophisticated times. Honey, the natural sweet sought by the peoples of the Stone Age, appears on the shelves of our supermarkets, and beeswax still has manifold uses. In the foreseeable future we shall still need the help of this little insect in pollinating our fruit and seed crops.

Maybe the honeybee was the first creature that man tried to domesticate, yet for all that long association he has never tamed it or changed its way of life one iota. The ways of bees were established millions of years before human beings, or indeed any other mammals, appeared. Complex as they are, their instincts have been fixed for so long that we are unable to alter them. Kept in a man-made hive and tended by him, they still behave exactly as they would in the wild. In fact a swarm often leaves a beekeeper's apiary and sets up a natural nest.

Through the study of their needs and activities, by providing them with partly furnished homes, feeding them in times of dearth, exercising some control over their swarming instinct, and placing them in locations where nectar is abundant, man directs their efforts to higher production. That is all.

bibliography

Butler, Colin. *The World of the Honeybee*. London: Collins, 1954.

Farb, Peter. *The Insects* (Life Nature Library). New York: Time, Inc., 1962.

Frisch, Karl von. *The Dancing Bees* (revised edition). London: Methuen & Co., 1954. New York: Harcourt, Brace & World, Inc., 1965.

Grout, Roy A. (ed.). *The Hive and the Honey Bee*. Hamilton, Illinois: Dadant & Sons, 1963.

Ribbands, C. Ronald. *The Behavior and Social Life of Honeybees*. Magnolia Mass: Peter Smith. New York: Dover Publications, Inc., 1965.

Tickner Edwardes, Rev. E. *The Lore of the Honey Bee*. London: Methuen & Co., 1944.

index

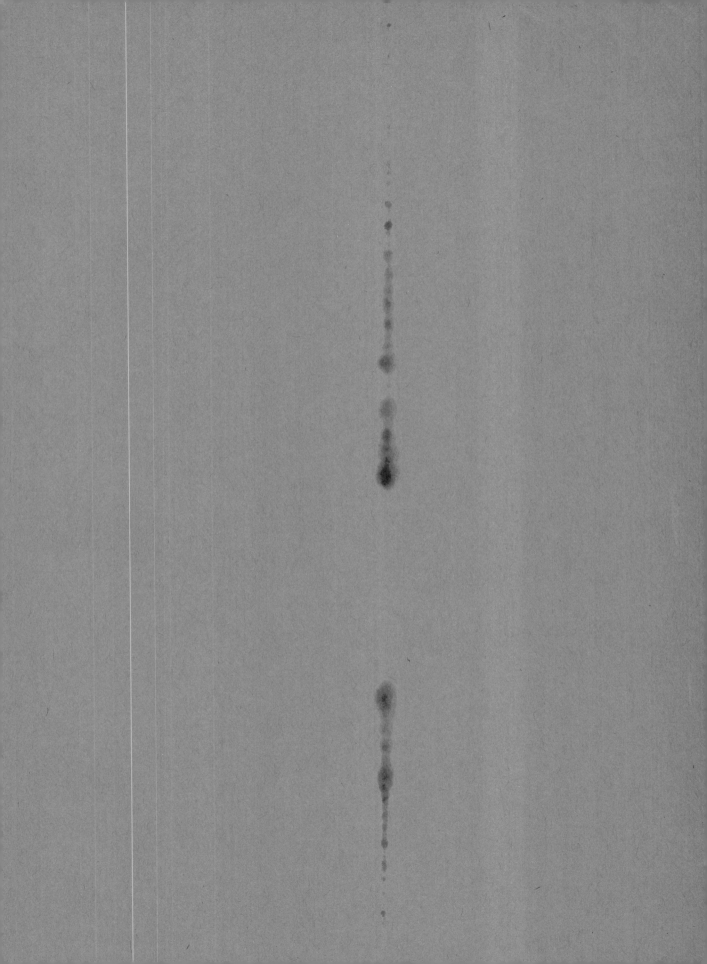